THE FUTURE MAKERS

of
he
is
on

Also edited by Peter Haining and available in the NEL series

DR. CALIGARI'S BLACK BOOK

The Future Makers

TALES OF FANTASY

Edited by
Peter Haining

NEW ENGLISH LIBRARY
TIMES MIRROR

For
MY FATHER
who taught me the value of heritage

First published in Great Britain by Sidgwick & Jackson Ltd., in 1968
This edition © by Peter Haining 1968

*

FIRST NEL EDITION SEPTEMBER 1969

*

NEL Books are published by
The New English Library Limited from Barnard's Inn, Holborn, London E.C.1.
Made and printed in Great Britain by Hunt Barnard & Co. Ltd., Aylesbury, Buck

45000369 8

CONTENTS

ACKNOWLEDGEMENTS

The editor is grateful to the following authors, their publishers and agents, for permission to reproduce copyright stories in this collection: "The Fourth Dimensional Demonstrator" by Murray Leinster © 1935 by Street and Smith Publications Inc., reprinted by permission of the author. "The Weapon Too Dreadful To Use" by Isaac Asimov © 1939 by *Amazing Stories*; reprinted by permission of the author. "Abreaction" by Theodore Sturgeon © 1939 by *Weird Tales*; reprinted by permission of the author. "The Piper" by Ray Bradbury © 1943 by *Thrilling Wonder Stories*; reprinted by permission of the author. "Columbus Was A Dope" by Robert Heinlein © 1947 by *Startling Stories*; reprinted by permission of the author. "Castaway" by Arthur C. Clarke © 1947 by *Fantasy*; reprinted by permission of the author. "The Hour of Battle" by Robert Sheckley © 1953 by *Space Science Fiction*; reprinted by permission of the author. "Equator" by Brian W. Aldiss © 1958 *Nova Publications Ltd*; reprinted by permission of the author.

INTRODUCTION

The eight contributors to this volume are probably today's most distinguished Science Fiction authors—their names are familiar to every fan and their reputations as storytellers have spread far beyond the bounds of the genre. They are all professionals, in fact; imaginative, painstaking, and dedicated writers who have mastered their craft and the ability to communicate a new idea, theme, or concept.

Today we take the brilliance of these eight men—for such it undoubtedly is—almost for granted. We wait eagerly for each new story or novel, confident in the knowledge that it will be at least as good, if not even better, than previous works. They can never over-produce where the vociferous fan is concerned—but wisely do not even try. Yet, like all true craftsmen, they did go through a period of apprenticeship when their names meant very little to readers and they worked industriously through the pages of small magazines and in the face of discouragingly small payments to develop and perfect styles which are eventually to earn them their world-wide acclaim and attention.

This anthology is an excursion back in time to those early years of the eight men; a selection from the archives of Science Fiction of a group of stories which illustrate the formation of techniques which each man was making particularly his own. The tales which I have chosen are all typical of the kind which they produced during their apprenticeship; one or two are even their author's very first efforts. All have long been out of print and are probably, in the main, unknown to today's new generation of readers. They show styles emerging and imaginations beginning to range over new ground—but do not judge them against their author's most modern and highly-tempered work, rather for their own sake and their value as "period" Science Fiction. Nonetheless, I believe you will find the standard of them all is quite astonishing.

Meet, now, *The Future Makers*—for together these stories present a totally fresh angle on the men who have shaped modern S.F.

PETER HAINING
1968

THE FOURTH DIMENSIONAL DEMONSTRATOR

BY MURRAY LEINSTER

Murray Leinster is unquestionably "The Dean of Science Fiction Writers". In a life-time that spans over seventy years, he has won for himself an enduring reputation for writing stories of great imagination and often uncanny prophecy. His first published story in the genre, "The Runaway Skyscraper" appeared in 1919 and in the interim he has won a Hugo Award, been many times nominated a top writer in Science Fiction and Fantasy magazines and developed his private interest in science to such an extent that one of his inventions—a method for making films without sets in which actors perform against projected backgrounds—is continually put to use by American T.V. and film companies. But above all else, it is stories like the one here—which Sam Moskowitz calls "one of the funniest stories ever to appear in Science Fiction"—which have established for him a permanent place in the great hall of Science Fiction.

Pete Davidson was engaged to Miss Daisy Manners of the Green Paradise floor show. He had just inherited all the properties of an uncle who had been an authority on the fourth dimension, and he was the custodian of an unusually amiable kangaroo named Arthur. But still he was not happy; it showed this morning.

Inside his uncle's laboratory, Pete scribbled on paper. He added, and ran his hands through his hair in desperation. Then he subtracted, divided and multiplied. But the results were invariably problems as incapable of solution as his deceased relative's fourth-dimensional equations. From time to time a long, horse-like, hopeful face peered in at him. That was Thomas, his uncle's servant, whom Pete was afraid he had also inherited.

"Beg pardon, sir," said Thomas tentatively.

Pete leaned harassedly back in his chair.

"What is it, Thomas? What has Arthur been doing now?"

"He is browsing in the dahlias, sir. I wished to ask about lunch, sir. What shall I prepare?"

"Anything!" said Pete. "Anything at all! No. On second thought, trying to untangle Uncle Robert's affairs calls for brains. Give me something rich in phosphorus and vitamins; I need them."

"Yes, sir," said Thomas. "But the grocer, sir—"

"Again?" demanded Pete hopelessly.

"Yes, sir," said Thomas, coming into the laboratory. "I hoped, sir, that matters might be looking better."

Pete shook his head, regarding his calculations depressedly.

"They aren't. Cash to pay the grocer's bill is still a dim and misty hope. It is horrible, Thomas! I remembered my uncle as simply reeking with cash, and I thought the fourth dimension was mathematics, not debauchery. But Uncle Robert must have had positive orgies with quanta and space-time continua! I shan't break even on the heir business, let alone make a profit!"

Thomas made a noise suggesting sympathy.

"I could stand it for myself alone," said Pete gloomily. "Even Arthur, in his simple, kangaroo's heart, bears up well. But Daisy! There's the rub! Daisy!"

"Daisy, sir?"

"My fiancée," said Pete. "She's in the Green Paradise floor show. She is technically Arthur's owner. I told Daisy, Thomas, that I had inherited a fortune. And she's going to be disappointed."

"Too bad, sir," said Thomas.

"That statement is one of humorous underemphasis, Thomas. Daisy is not a person to take disappointments lightly. When I explain that my uncle's fortune has flown off into the fourth dimension, Daisy is going to look absent-minded and stop listening. Did you ever try to make love to a girl who looked absent-minded?"

"No, sir," said Thomas. "But about lunch, sir—"

"We'll have to pay for it. Damn!" Pete said morbidly. "I've just forty cents in my clothes, Thomas, and Arthur at least, mustn't be allowed to starve. Daisy wouldn't like it. Let's see!"

He moved away from the desk and surveyed the laboratory with a predatory air. It was not exactly a homey place. There was a skeletonlike thing of iron rods, some four feet high. Thomas had said it was a tesseract—a model of cube existing in four dimensions instead of three.

To Pete, it looked rather like a medieval instrument of torture—something to be used in theological argument with a heretic. Pete could not imagine anybody but his uncle wanting it. There were other pieces of apparatus of all sizes, but largely dismantled. They looked like the product of some one putting vast amounts of money and patience into an effort to do something which would be unsatisfactory when accomplished.

"There's nothing here to pawn," said Pete depressedly. "Not even anything I could use for a hand organ, with Arthur substituting for the monkey!"

"There's the demonstrator, sir," said Thomas hopefully. "Your

10

uncle finished it, sir, and it worked, and he had a stroke, sir."

"Cheerful!" said Pete. "What is this demonstrator? What's it supposed to do?"

"Why, sir, it demonstrates the fourth dimension," said Thomas. "It's your uncle's life work, sir."

"Then let's take a look at it," said Pete. "Maybe we can support ourselves demonstrating the fourth dimension in shop windows for advertising purposes. But I don't think Daisy will care for the career."

Thomas marched solemnly to a curtain just behind the desk. Pete had thought it hid a cupboard. He slid the cover back and displayed a huge contrivance which seemed to have the solitary virtue of completion. Pete could see a monstrous brass horseshoe all of seven feet high. It was apparently hollow and full of cryptic cogs and wheels. Beneath it there was a circular plate of inch-thick glass which seemed to be designed to revolve. Below that, in turn, there was a massive base to which ran certain copper tubes from a refrigerating unit out of an ice box.

Thomas turned on a switch and the unit began to purr. Pete watched.

"Your uncle talked to himself quite a bit about this, sir," said Thomas. "I gathered that it's quite a scientific triumph, sir. You see, sir, the fourth dimension is time."

"I'm glad to hear it explained so simply," said Pete.

"Yes, sir. As I understand it, sir, if one were motoring and saw a pretty girl about to step on a banana peel, sir, and if one wished to tip her off, so to speak, but didn't quite realize for—say, two minutes, until one had gone on half a mile—"

"The pretty girl would have stepped on the banana peel and nature would have taken its course," said Pete.

"Except for this demonstrator, sir. You see, to tip off the young lady one would have to retrace the half mile and the time too, sir, or one would be too late. That is, one would have to go back not only the half mile but the two minutes. And so your uncle, sir, built this demonstrator—"

"So he could cope with such a situation when it arose," finished Pete. "I see! But I'm afraid it won't settle our financial troubles."

The refrigeration unit ceased to purr. Thomas solemnly struck a safety match.

"If I may finish the demonstration, sir," he said hopefully. "I blow out this match, and put it on the glass plate between the ends of the horseshoe. The temperature's right, so it should work."

There were self-satisfied clucking sounds from the base of the machine. They went on for seconds. The huge glass plate suddenly revolved perhaps the eighth of a revolution. A humming noise began. It stopped. Suddenly there was another burnt safety match on the glass plate. The machine began to cluck triumphantly.

11

"You see, sir?" said Thomas. "It's produced another burnt match. Dragged it forward out of the past, sir. There was a burnt match at that spot, until the glass plate moved a few seconds ago. Like the girl and the banana peel, sir. The machine went back to the place where the match had been, and then it went back in time to where the match was, and then it brought it forward."

The plate turned another eighth of a revolution. The machine clucked and hummed. The humming stopped. There was a third burnt match on the glass plate. The clucking clatter began once more.

"It will keep that up indefinitely, sir," said Thomas hopefully.

"I begin," said Pete, "to see the true greatness of modern science. With only two tons of brass and steel, and at a cost of only a couple of hundred thousand dollars and a lifetime of effort, my Uncle Robert has left me a machine which will keep me supplied with burnt matches for years to come! Thomas, this machine is a scientific triumph!"

Thomas beamed.

"Splendid, sir! I'm glad you approve. And what shall I do about lunch, sir?"

The machine, having clucked and hummed appropriately, now produced a fourth burnt match and clucked more triumphantly still. It prepared to reach again into the hitherto unreachable past.

Pete looked reproachfully at the servant he had apparently inherited. He reached in his pocket and drew out his forty cents. Then the machine hummed. Pete jerked his head and stared at it.

"Speaking of science, now," he said an instant later. "I have a very commercial thought. I blush to contemplate it." He looked at the monstrous, clucking demonstrator of the fourth dimension. "Clear out of here for ten minutes, Thomas. I'm going to be busy!"

Thomas vanished. Pete turned off the demonstrator. He risked a nickel, placing it firmly on the inch-thick glass plate. The machine went on again. It clucked, hummed, ceased to hum—and there were two nickels. Pete added a dime to the second nickel. At the end of another cycle he ran his hand rather desperately through his hair and added his entire remaining wealth—a quarter. Then, after incredulously watching what happened, he began to pyramid.

Thomas tapped decorously some ten minutes later.

"Beg pardon, sir," he said hopefully. "About lunch, sir—"

Pete turned off the demonstrator. He gulped.

"Thomas," he said in careful calm, "I shall let you write the menu for lunch. Take a basketful of this small change and go shopping. And—Thomas, have you any item of currency larger than a quarter? A fifty-cent piece would be about right. I'd like to have something really impressive to show to Daisy when she comes."

Miss Daisy Manners of the Green Paradise floor show was just

12

the person to accept the fourth-dimensional demonstrator without question and to make full use of the results of modern scientific research. She greeted Pete abstractedly and interestedly asked just how much he'd inherited. And Pete took her to the laboratory. He unveiled the demonstrator.

"These are my jewels," said Pete impressively. "Darling, it's going to be a shock, but—have you got a quarter?"

"You've got nerve, asking me for money," said Daisy. "And if you lied about inheriting some money—"

Pete smiled tenderly upon her. He produced a quarter of his own.

"Watch, my dear! I'm doing this for you!"

He turned on the demonstrator and explained complacently as the first cluckings came from the base. The glass plate moved, a second quarter appeared, and Pete pyramided the two while he continued to explain. In the fraction of a minute, there were four quarters. Again Pete pyramided. There were eight quarters— sixteen, thirty-two, sixty-four, one hundred twenty-eight— At this point the stack collapsed and Pete shut off the switch.

"You see, my dear? Out of the fourth dimension to you! Uncle invested it, I inherited it, and—shall I change your money for you?"

Daisy did not look at all absent-minded now. Pete gave her a neat little sheaf of bank notes.

"And from now on, darling," he said cheerfully, "whenever you want money just come in here, start the machine—and there you are! Isn't that nice?"

"I want some more money now," said Daisy. "I have to buy a trousseau."

"I hoped you'd feel that way!" said Pete enthusiastically. "Here goes! And we have a reunion while the pennies roll in."

The demonstrator began to cluck and clatter with bills instead of quarters on the plate. Once, to be sure, it suspended all operations and the refrigeration unit purred busily for a time. Then it resumed its self-satisfied delving into the immediate past.

"I haven't been making any definite plans," explained Pete, "until I talked to you. Just getting things in line. But I've looked after Arthur carefully. You know how he loves cigarettes. He eats them, and though it may be eccentric in a kangaroo, they seem to agree with him. I've used the demonstrator to lay up a huge supply of cigarettes for him—his favorite brand, too. And I've been trying to build up a bank account. I thought it would seem strange if we bought a house on Park Avenue and just casually offered a trunkful of bank notes in payment. It might look as if we'd been running a snatch racket."

"Stupid!" said Daisy.

"What?"

"You could be pyramiding those bills like you did the quarters," said Daisy. "Then there'd be lots more of them!"

13

"Darling," said Pete fondly, "does it matter how much you have when I have so much?"

"Yes," said Daisy. "You might get angry with me."

"Never!" protested Pete. Then he added reminiscently, "Before we thought of the bank note idea, Thomas and I filled up the coal bin with quarters and half dollars. They're still there."

"Gold pieces would be nice," suggested Daisy, thinking hard, "if you could get hold of some. Maybe we could."

"Ah!" said Pete. "But Thomas had a gold filling in one tooth. We took it out and ran it up to half a pound or so. Then we melted that into a little brick and put it on the demonstrator. Darling, you'd really be surprised if you looked in the woodshed."

"And there's jewelry," said Daisy. "It would be faster still!"

"If you feel in the mood for jewelry," said Pete tenderly, "just look in the vegetable bin. We'd about run out of storage space when the idea occurred to us."

"I think," said Daisy enthusiastically, "we'd better get married right away. Don't you?"

"Sure! Let's go and do it now! I'll get the car around!"

"Do, darling," said Daisy. "I'll watch the demonstrator."

Beaming, Pete kissed her ecstatically and rushed from the laboratory. He rang for Thomas, and rang again. It was not until the third ring that Thomas appeared. And Thomas was very pale. He said agitatedly:

"Beg pardon, sir, but shall I pack your bag?"

"I'm going to be— Pack my bag? What for?"

"We're going to be arrested, sir," said Thomas. He gulped. "I thought you might want it, sir. An acquaintance in the village, sir, believes we are among the lower-numbered public enemies, sir, and respects us accordingly. He telephoned me the news."

"Thomas, have you been drinking?"

"No, sir," said Thomas pallidly. "Not yet, sir. But it is a splendid suggestion, thank you, sir." Then he said desperately: "It's the money, sir—the bank notes. If you recall, we never changed but one lot of silver into notes, sir. We got a one, a five, a ten and so on, sir."

"Of course," said Pete. "That was all we needed. Why not?"

"It's the serial number, sir! All the one-dollar bills the demonstrator turned out have the same serial number—and all the fives and tens and the rest, sir. Some person with a hobby for looking for kidnap bills, sir, found he had several with the same number. The secret service has traced them back. They're coming for us, sir. The penalty for counterfeiting is twenty years, sir. My—my friend in the village asked if we intended to shoot it out with them, sir, because if so he'd like to watch."

Thomas wrung his hands. Pete stared at him.

"Come to think of it," he said meditatively, "they are counterfeits. It hadn't occurred to me before. We'll have to plead guilty, Thomas. And perhaps Daisy won't want to marry me if I'm going to prison. I'll go tell her the news."

Then he stared. He heard Daisy's voice, speaking very angrily. An instant later the sound grew louder. It became a continuous, shrill, soprano babble. It grew louder yet. Pete ran.

He burst into the laboratory and was stunned. The demonstrator was still running. Daisy had seen Pete piling up the bills as they were turned out, pyramiding to make the next pile larger. She had evidently essayed the same feat. But the pile was a bit unwieldly, now, and Daisy had climbed on the glass plate. She had come into the scope of the demonstrator's action.

There were three of her in the laboratory when Pete first entered. As he froze in horror, the three became four. The demonstrator clucked and hummed what was almost a hoot of triumph. Then it produced a fifth Daisy. Pete dashed frantically forward and turned off the switch just too late to prevent the appearance of a sixth copy of Miss Daisy Manners of the Green Paradise floor show. She made a splendid sister act, but Pete gazed in paralysed horror at this plethora of his heart's desire.

Because all of Daisy was identical, with not only the same exterior and—so to speak—the same serial number, but with the same opinions and convictions. And all six of Daisy were convinced that they, individually, owned the heap of bank notes now on the glass plate. All six of her were trying to get it. And Daisy was quarreling furiously with herself. She was telling herself what she thought of herself, in fact, and on the whole her opinion was not flattering.

Arthur, like Daisy, possessed a fortunate disposition. He was not one of those kangaroos who go around looking for things to be upset about. He browsed peacefully upon the lawn, eating up the dahlias and now and again hopping over the six-foot hedge in hopes that there might be a dog come along the lane to bark at him. Or, failing to see a dog, that somebody might have come by who would drop a cigarette butt that he might salvage.

At his first coming to this place, both pleasing events had been frequent. The average unwarned passer-by, on seeing a five-foot kangaroo soaring toward him in this part of the world, did have a tendency to throw down everything and run. Sometimes, among the things he threw down was a cigarette.

There had been a good supply of dogs, too, but they didn't seem to care to play with Arthur any more. Arthur's idea of playfulness with a strange dog—especially one that barked at him— was to grab him with both front paws and then kick the living daylights out of him.

Arthur browsed, and was somewhat bored. Because of his boredom he was likely to take a hand in almost anything that turned up. There was a riot going on in the laboratory, but Arthur did not care for family quarrels. He was interested, however, in the government officers when they arrived. There were two of them and they came in a roadster. They stopped at the gate and marched truculently up to the front door.

Arthur came hopping around from the back just as they knocked thunderously. He'd been back there digging up a few incipient cabbages of Thomas' planting, to see why they didn't grow faster. He soared at least an easy thirty feet, and propped himself on his tail to look interestedly at the visotors.

"G-good God!" said the short, squat officer. He had been smoking a cigarette. He threw it down and grabbed his gun.

That was his mistake. Arthur liked cigarettes. This one was a mere fifteen feet from him. He soared toward it.

The government man squawked, seeing Arthur in mid-air and heading straight for him. Arthur looked rather alarming, just then. The officer fired recklessly, missing Arthur. And Arthur remained calm. To him, the shots were not threats. They were merely the noises made by an automobile whose carburetor needed adjustment. He landed blandly, almost on the officer's toes—and the officer attacked him hysterically with fist and clubbed gun.

Arthur was an amiable kangaroo, but he resented the attack, actively.

The short, squat officer squawked again as Arthur grabbed him with his forepaws. His companion backed against the door, prepared to sell his life dearly. But then—and the two things happened at once—while Arthur proceeded to kick the living daylights out of the short, squat officer, Thomas resignedly opened the door behind the other and he fell backward suddenly and knocked himself cold against the doorstep.

Some fifteen minutes later the short, squat officer said gloomily: "It was a bum steer. Thanks for pulling that critter off me, and Casey's much obliged for the drinks. But we're hunting a bunch of counterfeiters that have been turning out damn good phoney bills. The line led straight to you. You could have shot us. You didn't. So we got to do the work all over."

"I'm afraid," admitted Pete, "the trail would lead right back. Perhaps, as government officials, you can do something about the fourth-dimensional demonstrator. That's the guilty party. I'll show you."

He led the way to the laboratory. Arthur appeared, looking vengeful. The two officers looked apprehensive.

"Better give him a cigarette," said Pete. "He eats them. Then he'll be your friend for life."

"Hell, no!" said the short, squat man. "You keep between him

16

and me! Maybe Casey'll want to get friendly."

"No cigarettes," said Casey apprehensively. "Would a cigar do?"

"Rather heavy, for so early in the morning," considered Pete, "but you might try."

Arthur soared. He landed within two feet of Casey. Casey thrust a cigar at him. Arthur sniffed at it and accepted it. He put one end in his mouth and bit off the tip.

"There!" said Pete cheerful. "He likes it. Come on!"

They moved on to the laboratory. They entered—and tumult engulfed them. The demonstrator was running and Thomas—pale and despairing—supervised its action. The demonstrator was turning out currency by what was, approximately, wheelbarrow loads. As each load materialized from the fourth dimension, Thomas gathered it up and handed it to Daisy, who in theory was standing in line to receive it in equitable division. But Daisy was having a furious quarrel among herself, because some one or other of her had tried to cheat.

"These," said Pete calmly, "are my fiancée."

But the short, squat man saw loads of greenbacks appearing from nowhere. He drew out a short, squat revolver.

"You got a press turning out the stuff behind that wall, huh?" he said shrewdly. "I'll take a look!"

He thrust forward masterfully. He pushed Thomas aside and mounted the inch-thick glass plate. Pete reached, horrified, for the switch. But it was too late. The glass plate revolved one-eighth of a revolution. The demonstrator hummed gleefully; and the officer appeared in duplicate just as Pete's nerveless fingers cut off everything.

Both of the officers looked at each other in flat, incredulous stupefaction. Casey stared, and the hair rose from his head. Then Arthur put a front paw tentatively upon Casey's shoulder. Arthur had liked the cigar. The door to the laboratory had been left open. He had come in to ask for another cigar. But Casey was hopelessly unnerved. He yelled and fled, imagining Arthur in hot pursuit. He crashed into the model of a tesseract and entangled himself hopelessly.

Arthur was an amiable kangaroo, but he was sensitive. Casey's squeal of horror upset him. He leaped blindly, knocking Pete over on the switch and turning it on, and landing between the two stupefied copies of the other officer. They, sharing memories of Arthur, moved in panic just before the glass plate turned.

Arthur bounced down again at the demonstrator's hoot. The nearest copy of the short, squat man made a long, graceful leap and went flying out of the door. Pete struggled with the other, who waved his gun and demanded explanations, growing hoarse from his earnestness.

Pete attempted to explain in terms of pretty girls stepping on banana peels, but it struck the officer as irrelevant. He shouted hoarsely while another Arthur hopped down from the glass plate—while a third, and fourth, and fifth, and sixth, and seventh Arthur appeared on the scene.

He barked at Pete until screams from practically all of Daisy made him turn to see the laboratory overflowing with five-foot Arthurs, all very pleasantly astonished and anxious to make friends with himself so he could play.

Arthur was the only person who really approved the course events had taken. He had existed largely in his own society. But now his own company was numerous. From a solitary kangaroo, in fact, Arthur had become a good-sized herd. And in his happy excitement over the fact, Arthur forgot all decorum and began to play an hysterical form of disorganized leapfrog all about the laboratory.

The officer went down and became a take-off spot for the game. Daisy shrieked furiously. And Arthur—all of him—chose new points of vantage for his leaps until one of him chose the driving motor of the demonstrator. That industrious mechanism emitted bright sparks and bit him. And Arthur soared in terror through the window, followed by all the rest of himself, who still thought it part of the game.

In seconds, the laboratory was empty of Arthurs. But the demonstrator was making wierd, pained noises. Casey remained entangled in the bars of the tesseract, through which he gazed'with much the expression of an inmate of a padded cell. Only one of the short, squat officers remained in the building. He had no breath left. And Daisy was too angry to make a sound—all six of her. Pete alone was sanely calm.

"Well," he said philosophically, "things seem to have settled down a bit. But something's happened to the demonstrator."

"I'm sorry, sir," said Thomas pallidly, "I'm no hand at machinery."

One of Daisy said angrily to another of Daisy: "You've got a nerve! That money on the plate is mine!"

Both advanced. Three more, protesting indignantly, joined in the rush. The sixth—and it seemed to Pete that she must have been the original Daisy—hastily began to sneak what she could from the several piles accumulated by the others.

Meanwhile, the demonstrator made queer noises. And Pete despairingly investigated. He found where Arthur's leap had disarranged a handle which evidently controlled the motor speed of the demonstrator. At random, he pushed the handle. The demonstrator clucked relievedly. Then Pete realized in such terror that five of Daisy were on the glass plate. He tried to turn it off—but it was too late.

He closed his eyes, struggling to retain calmness, but admitting despair. He had been extremely fond of one Daisy. But six Daisies had been too much. Now, looking forward to eleven and——

A harsh voice grated in his ear.

"Huh! That's where you keep the press and the queer, huh—and trick mirrors so I see double? I'm going through that trapdoor where those girls went! And if there's any funny business on the other side, somebody gets hurt!"

The extra officer stepped up on the glass plate, inexplicably empty now. The demonstrator clucked. It hummed. The plate moved—backward! The officer vanished—at once, utterly. As he had come out of the past, he returned to it, intrepidly and equally by accident. Because one of Arthur had kicked the drive lever into neutral, and Pete had inadvertently shoved it into reverse. He saw the officer vanish and he knew where the supernumerary Daisies had gone—also where all embarrassing bank notes would go. He sighed in relief.

But Casey—untangled from the tesseract—was not relieved. He tore loose from Thomas' helpful fingers and fled to the car. There he found his companion, staring at nineteen Arthurs playing leapfrog over the garage. After explanations the government men would be more upset still. Pete saw the roadster drive away, wabbling.

"I don't think they'll come back, sir," said Thomas hopefully.

"Neither do I," said Pete in a fine, high calm. He turned to the remaining Daisy, scared but still acquisitive. "Darling," he said tenderly, "all those bank notes are counterfeit, as it develops. We'll have to put them all back and struggle along with the contents of the woodshed and the vegetable bin."

Daisy tried to look absent-minded, and failed.

"I think you've got nerve!" said Daisy indignantly.

THE WEAPON TOO DREADFUL TO USE

BY ISAAC ASIMOV

Here is a rare orchid indeed: the very first published story by *Isaac Asimov*—penned at the tender age of 17. Born in 1920 at Petrovich, a Russian suburb, young Isaac moved with his family to America when he was three, and six years later had discovered Science Fiction through the pages of "Amazing Stories". He was immediately drawn to the genre and once he had begun writing tales himself never looked back. His star now glows brightly in the S.F. heaven—despite the fact that his serious writing on scientific topics has almost brought the flow of his short stories to a standstill—and throughout fandom he is known almost with reverence as "The Good Doctor". The journey you will undertake in the following pages clearly shows a fine talent beginning to blossom.

Karl Frantor found the prospect a terribly dismal one. From low-hanging clouds, fell eternal misty rain; squat, rubbery vegetation with its dull, reddish-brown colour stretched away in all directions. Now and then a Hop-scotch Bird fluttered wildly above them, emitting plaintive squawks as it went.

Karl turned his head to gaze at the tiny dome of *Aphrodopolis*, largest city on Venus.

"God," he muttered, "even the dome is better than this awful world out here." He pulled the rubberized fabric of his coat closer about him, "I'll be glad to get back to Earth again."

He turned to the slight figure of Antil, the Venusian, "When are we coming to the ruins, Antil?"

There was no answer and Karl noticed the tear that rolled down the Venusian's green, puckered cheeks. Another glistened in the large, lemur-like eyes; soft, incredibly beautiful eyes.

The Earthman's voice softened. "Sorry, Antil, I didn't mean to say anything against Venus."

Antil turned his green face toward Karl, "It was not that, my friend. Naturally, you would not find much to admire in an alien world. I, however, love Venus, and I weep because I am overcome with its beauty." The words came fluently but with the inevitable distortion caused by vocal cords unfitted for harsh languages.

"I know it seems incomprehensible to you," Antil continued,

20

"but to me Venus is a paradise, a golden land—I cannot express my feelings for it properly."

"Yet there are some that say only Earthmen can love." Karl's sympathy was strong and sincere.

The Venusian shook his head sadly. "There is much besides the capacity to feel emotion that your people deny us."

Karl changed the subject hurriedly. "Tell me, Antil, doesn't Venus present a dull aspect even to you. You've been to Earth and should know. How can this eternity of brown and grey compare to the living, warm colours of Earth?"

"It is far more beautiful to me. You forget that my colour sense is so enormously different from yours.* How can I explain the beauties, the wealth of colour in which this landscape abounds?" He fell silent, lost in the wonders he spoke of, while to the Terrestrial the deadly, melancholy grey remained unchanged.

"Someday," Antil's voice came as from a person in a dream, "Venus will once more belong to he Venusians. The Earthlings shall no longer rule us, and the glory of our ancestors shall return to us."

Karl laughed. "Come, now, Antil, you speak like a member of the Green Bands, that are giving the government so much trouble. I thought you didn't believe in violence."

"I don't, Karl," Antil's eyes were grave and rather frightened, "but the extremists are gaining power, and I fear the worst. And if—if open rebellion against Earth breaks out, I *must* join them."

"But you disagree with them."

"Yes, of course," he shrugged his shoulders, a gesture he had learned from Earthmen, "we can gain nothing by violence. There are five billion of you and scarcely a hundred million of us. You have resources and weapons while we have none. It would be a fool's venture and even should we win, we might leave such a heritage of hatred that there could never be peace between our two planets."

"Then why join them?"

"Because I am a Venusian."

The Earthman burst into laughter again. "Patriotism, it seems, is as irrational on Venus as on Earth. But come, let us proceed to the ruins of your ancient city. Are we nearly there?"

"Yes," answered Antil, "it's a matter of little more than an Earth mile now. Remember, however, that you are to disturb nothing. The ruins of *Ash-taz-zor* are sacred to us, as the sole existing remnant of the time when we, too, were a great race, rather than the degenerate remains of one."

They walked on in silence, slogging through the soft earth beneath, dodging the writhing roots of the Snaketree, and giving

* The Venusian eye can distinguish between two tints, the wave-lengths of which differ by as little as five Angstrom units. They see thousands of colours to which Earthmen are blind.—Author.

21

the occasional Tumbling Vines they passed a wide berth.

It was Antil then who resumed conversation.

"Poor Venus." His quiet, wistful voice was sad. "Fifty years ago the Earthman came with promises of peace and plenty—and we believed. We showed them the emerald mines and the *juju* weed and their eyes glittered with desire. More and more came, and their arrogance grew. And now—"

"It's too bad, Antil," Karl said, "but you really feel too strongly about it."

"Too strongly! Are we allowed to vote? Have we any representation at all in the Venusian Provincial Congress? Aren't there laws against Venusians riding in the same stratocars as Earthlings, or eating in the same hotel, or living in the same house? Are not all colleges closed to us? Aren't the best and most fertile parts of the planet pre-empted by Earthlings? Are there any rights *at all* that Terrestrials allow us upon our *own* planet?"

"What you say is perfectly true, and I deplore it. But similar conditions once existed on Earth with regard to certain so-called 'inferior races', and in time, all those disabilities were removed until today total equality reigns. Remember, too, that the intelligent people of Earth are on your side. Have I, for instance, ever displayed any prejudice against a Venusian?"

"No, Karl, you know you haven't. But how many intelligent men are there? On Earth, it took long and weary millennia, filled with war and suffering, before equality was established. What if Venus refuses to wait those millennia?"

Karl frowned, "You're right, of course, but you must wait. What else can you do?"

"I don't know—I don't know," Antil's voice trailed into silence.

Suddenly, Karl wished he hadn't started on this trip to the ruins of mysterious *Ash-taz-zor*. The maddeningly monotonous terrain, the just grievances of Antil had served to depress him greatly. He was about to call the whole thing off when the Venusian raised his webbed fingers to point out a mound of earth ahead.

"That's the entrance," he said; "*Ash-taz-zor* has been buried under the soil for uncounted thousands of years, and only Venusians know of it. You're the first Earthman ever to see it."

"I shall keep it absolutely secret, Antil. I have promised."

"Come then."

Antil brushed aside the lush vegetation to reveal a narrow entrance between two boulders and beckoned to Karl to follow. Into a narrow, damp corridor they crept. Antil drew from his pouch a small Atomite lamp, which cast its pearly white glow upon walls of dripping stone.

"These corridors and burrows," he said, "were dug three centuries ago by our ancestors who considered the city a holy place. Of late, however, we have neglected it. I was the first to

22

visit it in a long, long time. Perhaps that is another sign of our degeneracy."

For over a hundred yards they walked on straight ahead; then the corridors flared out into a lofty dome. Karl gasped at the view before him. There were the remains of buildings, architectural marvels unrivalled on Earth since the days of Periclean Athens. But all lay in shattered ruins, so that only a hint of the city's magnificence remained.

Antil led the way across the open space and plunged into another burrow that twisted its way for half a mile through soil and rock. Here and there, side corridors branched off, and once or twice Karl caught glimpses of ruined structures. He would have investigated had not Antil kept him on the path.

Again they emerged, this time before a low, sprawling building constructed of a smooth, green stone. Its right wing was utterly smashed, but the rest seemed scarcely touched.

The Venusian's eyes shone; his slight form straightened with pride. "This is what corresponds to a modern museum of arts and sciences. In this you shall see the past greatness and culture of Venus."

With high excitement, Karl entered—the first Earthman ever to see these ancient achievements. The interior, he found, was divided into a series of deep alcoves, branching out from the long central colonnade. The ceiling was one great painting that showed dimly in the light of the Atomite lamp.

Lost in wonder, the Earthman wandered through the alcoves. There was an extraordinary sense of strangeness to the sculptures and paintings about him, an unearthliness that doubled their beauty.

Karl realized that he missed something vital in Venusian art simply because of the lack of common ground between his own culture and theirs, but he could appreciate the technical excellence of the work. Especially, did he admire the colourwork of the paintings which went far beyond anything he had ever seen on Earth. Cracked, faded, and scaling though they were, there was a blending and a harmony about them that was superb.

"What wouldn't Michelangelo have given," he said to Antil, "to have the marvellous colour perception of the Venusian eye."

Antil inflated his chest with happiness. "Every race has its own attributes. I have often wished *my* ears could distinguish the slight tones and pitches of sound the way it is said Earthmen can. Perhaps I would then be able to understand what it is that is so pleasing about your Terrestrial music. As it is, its noise is dreadfully monotonous to me."

They passed on, and every minute Karl's opinion of Venusian culture mounted higher. There were long, narrow strips of thin metal, bound together, covered with the lines and ovals of Venusian script—thousands upon thousands of them. In them, Karl knew, might lie such secrets as the scientists of Earth would give half their lives to know.

Then, when Antil pointed out a tiny six-inch-high affair, and said that, according to the inscription, it was some type of atomic converter with an efficiency several times any of the current Terrestrial models, Karl exploded.

"Why don't you reveal these secrets to Earth? If they only knew your accomplishments in ages past. Venusians would occupy a far higher place then they do now."

"They would make use of our knowledge of former days, yes," Antil replied bitterly, "but they would never release their stranglehold on Venus and its people. I hope you are not forgetting your promise of absolute secrecy."

"No, I'll keep quiet, but I think you're making a mistake."

"I think not," Antil turned to leave the alcove but Karl called to him to wait.

"Aren't we going into this little room here?" he asked.

Antil whirled, eyes staring, "Room? What room are you talking about? There's no room here."

Karl's eyebrows shot up in surprise as he mutely pointed out the narrow crack that extended half way up the rear wall.

The Venusian muttered something beneath his breath and fell to his knees, delicate fingers probing the crack.

"Help me, Karl. This door was never meant to be opened, I think. At least there is no record of its being here, and I know the ruins of *Ash-taz-zor* perhaps better than any other of my people."

The two pushed against the section of the wall, which gave backward with groaning reluctance for a short distance, then yielded suddenly so as to catapult them into the tiny, almost empty cubicle beyond. They regained their feet and stared about.

The Earthman pointed out broken, ragged rust-streaks on the floor, and along the line where door joined wall. "Your people seem to have sealed this room up pretty effectively. Only the rust of eons broke the bonds. You'd think they had some sort of secret stored here."

Antil shook his green head. "There was no evidence of a door last time I was here. However—" he raised the Atomite lamp up high and surveyed the room rapidly, "there doesn't seem to be anything here, anyway."

He was right. Aside from a nondescript oblong chest that squatted on six stubby legs, the place contained only unbelievable quantities of dust and the musty, almost suffocating smell of long-shut-up tombs.

Karl approached the chest, tried to move it from the corner

24

where it stood. It didn't budge, but the cover slipped under his pressing fingers.

"The cover's removable, Antil. Look!" He pointed to a shallow compartment within, which contained a square slab of some glassy substance and five six-inch-long cylinders, resembling fountain-pens.

Antil shrieked with delight when he saw these objects and for the first time since Karl knew him, lapsed into sibilant Venusian gibberish. He removed the glassy slab and inspected it closely. Karl, his curiosity aroused, did likewise. It was covered with closely-spaced, vari-coloured dots, but there seemed no reason for Antil's extreme glee.

"What is it, Antil?"

"It is a complete document in our ancient ceremonial language. Up to now we have never had more than disjointed fragments. This is a great find."

"Can you decipher it?" Karl regarded the object with more respect.

"I think I can. It is a dead language and I know little more than a smattering. You see, it is a colour language. Each word is designated by a combination of two, and sometimes three, coloured dots. The colours are finely differentiated, though, and a Terrestrial, even if he had the key to the language, would have to use a spectroscope to read it."

"Can you work on it now?"

"I think so, Karl. The Atomite lamp approximates normal daylight very closely, and I ought to have no trouble with it. However, it may take me quite a time; so perhaps you'd better continue your investigation. There's no danger of your getting lost, provided you remain inside this building."

Karl left, taking a second Atomite lamp with him, left Antil, the Venusian, bent over the ancient manuscript, deciphering it slowly and painfully.

Two hours passed before the Earthman returned; but when he did, Antil had scarcely changed his position. Yet, now, there was a look of horror on the Venusian's face that had not been there before. The "colour" message lay at his feet, disregarded. The noisy entrance of the Earthman made no impression upon him. As if ossified, he sat in unmoving, staring fright.

Karl jumped to his side. "Antil, Antil, what's wrong?"

Antil's head, turned slowly, as though moving through viscous liquid, and his eyes gazed unseeingly at his friend. Karl grasped the other's thin shoulders and shook him unmercifully.

The Venusian came to his senses. Writhing out of Karl's grasp he sprang to his feet. From the desk in the corner he removed the five cylindrical objects, handling them with a queer sort of re-

25

luctance, placing them in his pouch. There, likewise, did he put the slab he had deciphered.

Having done this, he replaced the cover on the chest and motioned Karl out of the room. "We must go now. Already we have stayed too long." His voice had an odd, frightened tone about it that made the Earthman uncomfortable.

Silently, they retraced their steps until once more they stood upon the soaked surface of Venus. It was still day, but twilight was near. Karl felt a growing hunger. They would need to hurry if they expected to reach *Aphrodopolis* before the coming of night. Karl turned up the collar of his slicker, pulled his rubberized cap low over his forehead and set out.

Mile after mile passed by and the domed city once more rose upon the grey horizon. The Earthman chewed at damp ham sandwiches, wished fervently for the comfortable dryness of *Aphrodopolis*. Through it all, the normally friendly Venusian maintained a stony silence, vouchsafing not so much as a glance upon his companion.

Karl accepted this philosophically. He had a far higher regard for Venusians than the great majority of Earthmen, but even he experienced a faint disdain for the ultra-emotional character of Antil and his kind. This brooding silence was but a manifestation of feelings that in Karl would perhaps have resulted in no more than a sigh or a frown. Realizing this, Antil's mood scarcely affected him.

Yet the memory of the haunting fright in Antil's eyes aroused a faint unease. It had come after the translation of that queer slab. What secret could have been revealed in that message by those scientific progenitors of the Venusians?

It was with some diffidence that Karl finally persuaded himself to ask, "What did the slab say, Antil? It must be interesting, I judge, considering that you've taken it with you."

Antil's reply was simply a sign to hurry, and the Venusian thereupon plunged into the gathering darkness with redoubled speed. Karl was puzzled and rather hurt. He made no further attempt at conversation for the duration of the trip.

When they reached *Aphrodopolis*, however, the Venusian broke his silence. His puckered face, drawn and haggard, turned to Karl with the expression of one who has come to a painful decision.

"Karl," he said, "we have been friends, so I wish to give you a bit of friendly advice. You are going to leave for Earth next week. I know your father is high in the councils of the Planetary President. You yourself will probably be a personage of importance in the not-too-distant future. Since this is so, I beg you earnestly to use every atom of your influence to a moderation of Earth's attitude toward Venus. I, in my turn, being an hereditary noble of the largest tribe on Venus, shall do my utmost to repress all attempts at violence."

The other frowned. "There seems to be something behind all this. I don't get it at all. What are you trying to say?"

"Just this. Unless conditions are bettered—and soon—Venus will rise in revolt. In that case, I will have no choice but to place my services at her feet, and then Venus will no longer be defenceless."

These words served only to amuse the Earthman. "Come, Antil. Your patriotism is admirable, and your grievances justified, but melodrama and chauvinism don't go with me. I am, above all, a realist."

There was a terrible earnestness in the Venusian's voice. "Believe me, Karl, when I say nothing is more real than what I tell you now. In case of a Venusian revolt, I cannot vouch for Earth's safety."

"Earth's safety!" The enormity of this stunned Karl.

"Yes," continued Antil, "for I may be forced to destroy Earth. There you have it." With this, he wheeled and plunged into the underbrush on the way back to the little Venusian village outside the great dome.

Five years passed—years of turbulent unrest, and Venus stirred in its sleep like an awakening volcano. The short-sighted Terrestrial masters of *Aphrodopolis*, *Venusia*, and other domed cities cheerfully disregarded all danger signals. When they thought of the little green Venusians at all, it was with a disdainful grimace as if to say, "Oh, THOSE things!"

But "those things" were finally pushed beyond endurance, and the nationalistic Green Bands became increasingly vociferous with every passing day. Then, on one grey day, not unlike the grey days preceding, crowds of natives swarmed upon the cities in organized rebellion.

The smaller domes, caught by surprise, succumbed. In rapid succession *New Washington*, *Mount Vulcan*, and *St. Denis* were taken together with the entire eastern continent. Before the reeling Terrestrials realized what was happening, half of Venus was no longer theirs.

Earth, shocked and stunned by this sudden emergency—which, of course, should have been foreseen—sent arms and supplies to the inhabitants of the remaining beleaguered towns and began to equip a great space fleet for the recovery of the lost territory.

Earth was annoyed but not frightened, knowing that ground lost by surprise could easily be regained at leisure, and that ground not now lost would never be lost. Or such, at least, was the belief.

Imagine, then, the stupefaction of Earth's leaders as no pause came in the Venusian advance. *Venusia City* had been amply stocked with weapons and food; her outer defences were up, the men at their posts. A tiny army of naked, unarmed natives approached and demanded unconditional surrender. *Venusia* refused haughtily, and the messages to Earth were mirthful in their references to the unarmed natives who had become so recklessly flushed with success.

Then, suddenly, no more messages were received, and the natives took over *Venusia*.

The events at *Venusia* were duplicated, over and over again, at what should have been impregnable fortresses. Even *Aphrodopolis* itself, with half a million population, fell to a pitiful five hundred Venusians. This, in spite of the fact that every weapon known to Earth was available to the defenders.

The Terrestrial Government suppressed the facts, and Earth itself remained unsuspecting of the strange events on Venus; but in the inner councils, statesmen frowned as they listened to the strange words of Karl Frantor, son of the Minister of Education.

Jan Heersen, Minister of War, rose in anger at the conclusion of the report.

"Do you wish us to take seriously the random statement of a half-mad Greenie and make our peace with Venus on its own terms? That is definitely and absolutely impossible. What those damned beasts need is the mailed fist. Our fleet will blast them out of the Universe, and it is time that it were done."

"The blasting may not be so simple, Heersen," said the grey-haired, elder Frantor, rushing to his son's defence. "There are many of us who have all along claimed that the Government policy toward the Venusians was all wrong. Who knows what means of attack they have found and what, in revenge, they will do with it?"

"Fairy tales!" exclaimed Heersen. "You treat the Greenies as if they were people. They're animals and should be thankful for the benefits of civilization we brought them. Remember, we're treating them much better than some of our own Earth races were treated in our early history, the Red Indians for example."

Karl Frantor burst in once more in an agitated voice. "We must investigate, sirs! Antil's threat is too serious to disregard, no matter how silly it sounds—and in the light of the Venusian conquests, it sounds anything but silly. I propose that you send me with Admiral von Blumdorff, as a sort of envoy. Let me get to the bottom of this before we attack them."

The saturnine Earth President, Jules Debuc, spoke now for the first time. "Frantor's proposal is reasonable, at least. It shall be done. Are there any objections?"

There were none, though Heersen scowled and snorted angrily. Thus, a week later, Karl Frantor accompanied the space armada of Earth when it set off for the inner planet.

It was a strange Venus that greeted Karl after his five years' absence. It was still its old soaking self, its old dreary, monotony of white and grey, its scattering of domed cities—and yet how different.

Where before the haughty Terrestrials had moved in disdainful splendour among the cowering Venusians, now the natives maintained undisputed sway. *Aphrodopolis* was a native city entirely, and in the office of the former governor sat—Antil.

Karl eyed him doubtfully, scarcely knowing what to say. "I rather thought you might be king-pin," he managed at length. "You—the pacifist."

"The choice was not mine. It was that of circumstance," Antil replied. "But you! I did not expect *you* to be your planet's spokesman."

"It was to me that you made your silly threat years ago, and so it is I who was most pessimistic concerning your rebellion. I come, you see, not unaccompanied." His hand motioned vaguely upward where spaceships lazed motionless and threatening.

"You come to menace me?"

"No! To hear your aims and your terms."

"That is easily accomplished. Venus demands its independence and its acceptance by Earth as an equal and sovereign power. In return, we promise friendship, together with free and unrestricted trade."

"And you expect us to accept all that without a struggle."

"I hope you do—for Earth's own sake."

Karl scowled and threw himself back in his chair in annoyance, "For God's sake, Antil, the time for mysterious hints and bogies has passed. Show your hand. How did you overcome *Aphrodopolis* and the other cities so easily."

"We were forced to it, Karl. We did not desire it." Antil's voice was shrill with agitation. "They would not accept our fair terms of surrender and began to shoot their Tonite guns. We—we had to use the—the weapon. We had to kill most of them afterward—out of mercy."

"I don't follow. What weapon are you talking about?"

"Do you remember that time in the ruins of *Ash-taz-zor*, Karl? The hidden room; the ancient inscription; the five little rods."

Karl nodded sombrely. "I thought so, but I wasn't sure."

"It was a horrible weapon, Karl." Antil hurried on as if the mere thought of it were not to be endured. "The ancients discovered it—but never used it. They hid it instead, and why they did not destroy it, I can't imagine. I wish they had destroyed it; I really do. But they didn't and I found it and I must use it—for the good of Venus."

His voice sank to a whisper, but with a manifest effort he nerved himself to the task of explanation. "The little harmless rods you saw then, Karl, were capable of producing a force field of some unknown nature (the ancients wisely refused to be explicit there)

29

which has the power of disconnecting brain from mind."

"What?" Karl stared in open-mouthed surprise. "What *are* you talking about?"

"Why, you must know that the brain is merely the *seat* of the mind, and not the mind itself. The nature of 'mind' is a mystery, unknown even to our ancients; but whatever it is, it uses the brain as its intermediary to the world of matter."

"I see. And your weapon divorces mind from brain—renders mind helpless—a space-pilot without his controls."

Antil nodded solemnly. "Have you ever seen a decerebrated animal?" he asked suddenly.

"Why, yes, a dog—in my bio course back in college."

"Come, then, I will show you a decerebrated human."

Karl followed the Venusian to an elevator. As he shot downward to the lowest level—the prison level—his mind was in a turmoil. Torn between horror and fury, he had alternate impulses of unreasoning desire to escape and almost insuperable yearnings to slay the Venusian at his side. In a daze, he left the cubicle and followed Antil down a gloomy corridor, winding its way between rows of tiny, barred cells.

"There." Antil's voice roused Karl as would a sudden stream of cold water. He followed the pointing webbed hand and stared in fascinated revulsion at the human figure revealed.

It was human, undoubtedly, in form—but inhuman, nevertheless. It (Karl could not imagine it as "he") sat dumbly on the floor, large staring eyes never leaving the blank wall before him. Eyes that were empty of soul, loose lips from which saliva drooled, fingers that moved aimlessly. Nauseated, Karl turned his head hastily.

"He is not exactly decerebrated." Antil's voice was low. "Organically, his brain is perfect and unharmed. It is merely—disconnected."

"How does it live, Antil? Why doesn't it die?"

"Because the autonomic system is untouched. Stand him up and he will remain balanced. Push him and he will regain his balance. His heart beats. He breathes. If you put food in his mouth, he will swallow, though he would die of starvation before performing the voluntary act of eating food that has been placed before him. It is life—of a sort; but it were better dead, for the disconnection is permanent."

"It is horrible—horrible."

"It is worse than you think. I feel convinced that somewhere within that shell of humanity, the mind, unharmed, still exists. Imprisoned helplessly in a body it cannot control, what must be that mind's torture?"

Karl stiffened suddenly. "You shan't overcome Earth by sheer unspeakable brutality. It is an unbelievably cruel weapon but no more deadly than any of a dozen of ours. You shall pay for this."

"Please, Karl, you have no conception of one-millionth of the deadliness of the 'Disconnection Field'. The Field is independent of space, and perhaps of time, too, so that its range can be extended almost indefinitely. Do you know that it required merely one discharge of the weapon to render every warm-blooded creature in *Aphrodopolis* helpless?" Antil's voice rose tensely. "Do you know that I am able to bathe ALL EARTH in the Field—to render all your teeming billions the duplicate of that dead-alive hulk in there AT ONE STROKE."

Karl did not recognize his own voice as he rasped, "Fiend! Are you the only one who knows the secret of this damnable Field?"

Antil burst into a hollow laugh. "Yes, Karl, the blame rests on me, alone. Yet killing me will not help. If I die, there are others who know where to find the inscription, others who have not my sympathy for Earth. I am perfectly safe from you, Karl, for my death would be the end of your world."

The Earthman was broken—utterly. Not a fragment of doubt as to the Venusian's power was left within him. "I yield," he muttered, "I yield. What shall I tell my people?"

"Tell them of my terms, and of what I could do if I wished."

Karl shrank from the Venusian as if his very touch was death, "I will tell them that."

"Tell them also, that Venus is not vindictive. We do not wish to use our weapon, for it is too dreadful to use. If they will give us our independence on our own terms, and allow us certain wise precautions against future re-enslavement, we will hurl each of our five guns and the explanatory inscription explaining it into the sun."

The Terrestrial's voice did not change from its toneless whisper. "I will tell them that."

Admiral von Blumdorff was as Prussian as his name, and his military code was the simple one of brute force. So it was quite natural that his reactions to Karl's report were explosive in their sarcastic derision.

"You forsaken fool," he raved at the young man. "This is what comes of talk, of words, of tomfoolery. You *dare* come back to me with this old-wives' tale of mysterious weapons, of untold force. Without any proof at all, you accept all that this damned Greenie tells you at absolute face value, and surrender abjectly. Couldn't *you* threaten, couldn't *you* bluff, couldn't *you* lie?"

"He didn't threaten, bluff, or lie," Karl answered warmly. "What he said was the gospel truth. If you had seen the decerebrated man—"

"Bah! That is the most inexcusable part of the whole cursed

business. To exhibit a lunatic to you, some perfectly normal mental defective, and to say, 'This is our weapon!' and for you to accept that without question! Did they do anything but talk? Did they demonstrate the weapon? Did they even show it to you?"

"Naturally not. The weapon is deadly. They're not going to kill a Venusian to satisfy me. As for showing me the weapon—well, would *you* show your ace-in-the-hole to the enemy? Now you answer *me* a few questions. Why is Antil so cocksure of himself? How did he conquer all Venus so easily?"

"I can't explain it I admit, but does that prove that *theirs* is the correct explanation? Anyhow, I'm sick of this talk. We're attacking now, and to hell with theories. I'll face them with Tonite projectiles and you can watch their bluff backfire in their ugly faces."

"But, Admiral, you *must* communicate my report to the President."

"I will—after I blow *Aphrodopolis* into kingdom come."

He turned on the central broadcasting unit. "Attention, all ships! Battle formation! We dive at *Aphrodopolis* with all Tonites blasting in fifteen minutes." Then he turned to the orderly. "Have Captain Larsen inform *Aphrodopolis* that they have fifteen minutes to hoist the white flag."

The minutes that ticked by after that were tense and nerve-wracking for Karl Frantor. He sat in bent silence, head buried in his hands and the faint click of the chronometer at the end of every minute sounded like a thunder-clap in his ears. He counted those clicks in a mumbling whisper—8—9—10. God!

Only five minutes to certain death! Or *was* it certain death? Was von Blumdorff right? Were the Venusians putting over a daring bluff?

An orderly catapulted into the room and saluted. "The Greenies have just answered, sir."

"Well," von Blumdorff leaned forward eagerly.

"They say, 'Urgently request fleet not to attack. If done, we shall not be responsible for the consequences.' "

"Is that all?" came the outraged shout.

"Yes, sir."

The Admiral burst into a sulphurous stream of profanity. "Why, the infernal gall of them," he shouted. "They dare bluff to the very end."

And as he finished, the fifteenth minute clicked off, and the mighty armada burst into motion. In streaking, orderly flight they shot down toward the cloudy shroud of the second planet. Von Blumdorff grinned in a grisly appreciation of the awesome view spread over the televisor—until the mathematically precise battle formation suddenly broke.

The Admiral stared and rubbed his eyes. The entire further half of the fleet had suddenly gone crazy. First, the ships wavered; then they veered and shot off at mad angles.

Then calls came in from the sane half of the fleet—reports that the left wing had ceased to respond to radio.

The attack on *Aphrodopolis* was immediately disrupted as the order went out to capture the ships that had run amok. Von Blumdorff stamped up and down and tore his hair. Karl Frantor cried out dully, "It is their weapon," and lapsed back into his former silence.

From *Aphrodopolis* came no word at all.

For two solid hours the remnant of the Terrestrial fleet battled their own ships. Following the aimless courses of the stricken vessels, they approached and grappled. Bound together then by rigid force, rocket blasts were applied until the insane flight of the others had been balanced and stopped. Fully twenty of the fleet were never caught; some continuing on some orbit about the sun, some shooting off into unknown space, a few crashing down to Venus.

When the remaining ships of the left wing were boarded, the unsuspecting boarding parties stopped short in horror. *Seventy-five staring, witless shells of humanity in each ship.* Not a single *human* being left.

Some of the first to enter screamed in horror and fled in a panic. Others merely retched and turned away their eyes. One officer took in the situation at a glance, calmly drew his Atomo-pistol and rayed every decerebrate in sight.

Admiral von Blumdorff was a stricken man; a pitiful, limp wreck of his former proud and blustering self, when he heard the worst. One of the decerebrates was brought to him, and he reeled back.

Karl Frantor gazed at him with red-rimmed eyes. "Well, Admiral, are you satisfied?"

But the Admiral made no answer. He drew his gun, and before anyone could stop him, shot himself through the head.

Once again Karl Frantor stood before a meeting of the President and his Cabinet, before a dispirited, frightened group of men. His report was definite and left no doubt as to the course that must now be followed.

President Debuc stared at the decerebrate brought in as an exhibit. "We are finished," he said. "We must surrender unconditionally, throw ourselves upon their mercy. But someday—," his eyes kindled in retribution.

"No, Mr. President!" Karl's voice rang out, "there shall be no someday. We must give the Venusians their simple due—liberty and independence. Bygones must be bygones—our dead have but paid for the half-century of Venusian slavery. After this, there must be a new order in the Solar System—the birth of a new day."

The President lowered his head in thought and then raised it again. "You are right," he answered with decision; "there shall be no thought of revenge."

Two months later the peace treaty was signed and Venus became what it has remained ever since—an independent and sovereign power. And with the signing of the treaty, a whirling speck shot out toward the sun. It was—the weapon too dreadful to use.

ABREACTION

BY THEODORE STURGEON

> Thwarted in his youthful desire to be a trapeze artist because
> of an enlarged heart, *Theodore Sturgeon* has instead become a
> gymnast with words, a juggler of ideas and a storytelling
> performer of great merit. Reared in a strictly religious home,
> Sturgeon found his one delight was in retreating to the library
> where he discovered the books of H. G. Wells and Jules Verne
> and these kindled his interest in fantasy. A lot of his early work—
> like the story here—first appeared in magazines such as
> "Weird Tales", but the Science Fiction publications were his
> chief delight and riding out a number of personal crises, he
> eventually emerged as one of the most inventive of all modern
> S.F. writers—a man admired both by the readers and his fellow
> writers. He has occasionally outraged the public with his sexual
> themes and unpredictable nature, but his by-line above a story
> is always a guarantee of a unique experience. "Abreaction"
> is no exception.

I sat at the controls of the big D-8 bulldozer, and I tried to remember. The airfield shoulder, built on a saltflat, stretched
around me. On to the west was a clump of buildings—the gas
station and grease rack. Near it was the skeletal silhouette of a
temporary weather observation post with its spinning velocimeter
and vane and windsock. Everything seemed normal, but there was
something *else*. . . .

I could remember people, beautiful people in shining, floating
garments. I remembered them as if I had seen them just a minute
ago, and yet at a distance; but the memories were of faces close—
close. One face—a golden girl; eyes and skin and hair three different shades of gold.

I shook my head so violently that it hurt. I was a bulldozer
operator. I was—what was I supposed to be doing? I looked
around me, saw the gravel spread behind me, the bare earth
ahead; knew, then, that I was spreading gravel with the machine.
But I seemed to—to— Look, without the physical fact of the half-
done job around me, I wouldn't have known why I was there
at all!

I knew where I had seen that girl, those people. I thought I
knew . . . but the thought was just where I couldn't reach it. My

mind put out searching tendrils for that knowledge of place, that was so certainly there, and the knowledge receded so that the tendrils stretched out thin and cracked with the effort, and my head ached from it.

A big trailer-type bottom-dump truck came hurtling and howling over the shoulder toward me, the huge fenderless driving wheels throwing clots of mud high in the air. The driver was a Puerto-Rican, a hefty middle-aged fellow. I knew him well. Well—didn't I? He threw out one arm, palm up, signalling "Where do you want it?" I pointed vaguely to the right, to the advancing edge of the spread gravel. He spun his steering wheel with one hand, put the other on the trip-lever on his steering column, keeping his eyes on my face. As he struck the edge of the gravel fill with his wheels I dropped my hand; he punched the lever and the bottom of the trailer opened up, streaming gravel out in a windrow thirty feet long and a foot deep—twelve cubic yards of it, delivered at full speed. The driver waved and headed off, the straightgut exhaust of his high-speed Diesel snorting and snarling as the rough ground bounced the man's foot on the accelerator.

I waved back at the Puerto-Rican—what was his name? I knew him, didn't I? He knew me, the way he waved as he left. His name—was it Paco? Cruz? Eulalio? Damn it, no, and I knew it as well as I knew my own—

But I didn't know my own name!

Oh hell, oh hell, I'm crazy. I'm scared. I'm scared crazy. What had happened to my head? . . . Everything whirled around me and without effort I remembered about the people in the shining clothes and as my mind closed on it, it evaporated again and there was nothing there.

Once when I was a kid in school I fell off the parallel bars and knocked myself out, and when I came to it was like this. I could see everything and feel and smell and taste anything, but I couldn't remember anything. Not for a minute. I would ask what had happened, and they would tell me, and five minutes later I'd ask again. They asked me my address so they could take me home, and I couldn't remember it. They got the address from the school files and took me home, and my feet found the way in and up four flights of stairs to our apartment—I didn't remember which way to go but my feet did. I went in and tried to tell my mother what was the matter with me and I couldn't remember, and she put me to bed and I woke four hours later perfectly all right again.

In a minute, there on the bulldozer, I didn't get over being scared but I began to get used to it, so I could think a little. I tried to remember everything at first, but that was too hard, so I tried to find something I could remember. I sat there and let my mind go quite blank. Right away there was something about a bottom-

36

dump truck and some gravel. It was there, clear enough, but I didn't know where it fit nor how far back. I looked around me and there was the windrow of gravel waiting to be spread. Then that was what the truck was for; and—had it just been there, or had I been sitting there for long, for ever so long, waiting to remember that I must spread it?

Then I saw that I could remember ideas, but not events. Events were there, yes, but not in order. No continuity. A year ago—a second ago—same thing. Nothing clear, nothing very real, all mixed up. Ideas were there whatever, and continuity didn't matter. That I could remember an idea, that I could know that a windrow of gravel meant that gravel must be spread; *that* was an idea, a condition of things which I could recognize. The truck's coming and going and dumping, that was an event. I knew it had happened because the gravel was there, but I didn't know when, or if anything had happened in between.

I looked at the controls and frowned. Could I remember what to do with them? This lever and that pedal—what did they mean to me? Nothing, and nothing again. . . .

I mustn't thing about that. I don't have to think about that. I must think about *what* I must do and not how I must do it. I've got to spread the stone. Here there is spread stone and there there is none, and at the edge of the spread stone is the windrow of gravel. So, watching it, seeing how it lay, I let my hands and feet remember about the levers and pedals. They throttled up, raised the blade off the ground, shifted into third gear, swung the three-ton mould-board and its twelve-foot cutting edge into the windrow. The blade loaded and gravel ran off the ends in two even rolls, and my right hand flicked to and away from me on the blade control, knowing how to raise it enough to let the gravel run out evenly underneath the cutting edge, not too high so that it would make a bobble in the fill for the tracks to teeter on when they reached it—for a bulldozer builds the road it walks on, and if the road is rough the machine see-saws forward and the blade cuts and fills to make waves which, when the tracks reach them, makes the machine see-saw and cut waves, which, when the tracks reach them . . . anyway, my hands knew what to do, and my feet; and they did it all the time when I could only see what was to be done, and could not understand the events of doing it.

This won't do, I thought desperately. I'm all right, I guess, because I can do my work. It's all laid out in front of me, and I know what has to be done and my hands and feet know how to do it; but suppose somebody comes and speaks to me or tells me to go somewhere else. I who can't even remember my own name. My hands and my feet have more sense than my head.

So I thought that I had to inventory everything I could trust, every-

37

thing I knew positively. What were the things I knew?

The machine was there and true, and the gravel, and the bottom-dump that brought it. My being there was a real thing. You have to start everything with the belief that you yourself exist.

The job, the work, they were true things.

Where was I?

I must be where I should be, where I belonged, for the bottom-dump driver knew me, knew I was there, knew I was waiting for stone to spread. The airfield was there, and the fact that it was unfinished. "Airfield" was like a corollary to me, with the runway and the windsock its supporting axioms, and I had no need to think further. The people in the shining garments, and the girl—

But there was nothing about them here. Nothing at all.

To spread stone was a thing I had to do. But was that all? It wasn't just spreading stone. I had to spread it to—to—

Not to help finish the airfield. It wasn't that. It was something else, something—

Oh. Oh! I had to spread stone to *get* somewhere.

I didn't want to go anywhere, except maybe to a place where I could think again, where I could know what was happening to me, where I could reach out with my mind and grasp those important things, like my name, and the name of the bottom-dump driver, Paco, or Cruz, or Eulalio or maybe even Emanualo von Hachmann de la Vega, or whatever. But being able to think straight again and know all these important things was arriving at a *state* of consciousness, not at a *place*. I knew, I knew, somehow I knew truly that to arrive at that state I had to arrive at a point.

Suddenly, overwhelmingly, I had a flash of knowledge about the point—not what it was, but how it was, and I screamed and hurt my throat and fell blindly back in the seat of the tractor trying to push away *how* it was.

My abdomen kneaded itself with the horror of it. I put my hands on my face and my hands and face were wet with sweat and tears. Afraid? Have you ever been afraid to die, seeing Death looking right at you; closer than that; have you seen Death turn away from you because He knows you must follow Him? Have you seen that and been afraid?

Well, this was worse. For this I'd hug Death to me, for He alone could spare me what would happen to me when I reached the place I was going to.

So I wouldn't spread stone.

I wouldn't do anything that would bring me closer to reaching the place where that thing would happen to me. *Had happened* to me. . . . I wouldn't do it. That was an important thing.

There was one other important thing. I must not go on like this, not knowing my name, and what the name of the bottom-dump driver was, and where this airfield and this base were, and all

38

those things.

These two things were the most important things in the world. In *this* world. . . . THIS world. . . .

This world, this world—*other* world. . . .

There was a desert all around me.

Ha! So the airfield wasn't real, and the bottom-dump wasn't real, and the animometer and the grease-racks weren't real. Ha! (why worry about the driver's name if he wasn't real?)

The bulldozer was real, though. I was sitting on it. The six big cylinders were ticking over, and the master-clutch lever was twitching rhythmically as if its lower end were buried in something that breathed. Otherwise—just desert, and some hills over there, and a sun which was too orange.

Think, now, think. This desert means something important. I wasn't surprised at being in the desert. That was important. This place in the desert was near something, near an awful something that would hurt me.

I looked all around me. I couldn't see it, but it was there, the something that would hurt so. I wouldn't go through that again—Again.

Again—that was an important thing. I wouldn't spread stone and reach that place. I wouldn't go through that which had happened to me even if I stayed crazy like I was for the rest of eternity. Let them put me away and tie me up and shake their heads over me and walk away and leave me, and put bars on the window to slice the light of the crooked moon into black and silver bars on the floor of my cell. I didn't care about all that. I could face the ache of wanting to know about my name and the name of the driver of the bottom-dump (he was a Puerto-Rican, so his name must be Villamil or Roberto, not Bucyrus-Erie or Caterpiller Thirteen Thousand) and the people in the shining clothes; I *was* facing all that, and I know how it hurt, but I would not go through that place again and be hurt so much more. Not again. Not again.

Again. Again again again. What is the again-ness of everything? Everything I am doing I am doing again. I could remember that feeling from before—years ago it used to happen to me every once in a while. You've never been to a certain village before, we'll say, and you come up over the crown of the hill on your bicycle and see the way the church is and the houses, and the turn of that crooked cobblestoned street, the shape and tone of the very flower-stems. You know that if you were asked, you could say how many pickets were in the white gate in the blue-and-white fence in the little house third from the corner. All the scientists nod and smile and say you did see it for the second time—a twentieth of a second after the first glimpse; and that the impact of familiarity

39

was built up in the next twentieth of a second. And you nod and smile too and say well, whaddaye know. But you know, you *know* you've seen that place before, no matter what they say.

That's the way I knew it, sitting there on my machine in the desert and not surprised, and having that feeling of againness; because I was remembering the last time the bottom-dump came to me there on the airfield shoulder, trailing a plume of blue smoke from the exhaust stack, bouncing and barking as it hurtled toward me. It meant nothing at first, remembering, that it came, nor that it was the same driver, the Puerto-Rican; and of course he was carrying the same sized load of the same material. All trips of the bottom-dump were pretty much the same. But there was one thing I remembered—*now* I remembered—

There was a grade-stake driven into the fill, to guide the depth of the gravel, and *it was no nearer to me than it had ever been.* So that hadn't been the same bottom-dump, back another time. It was the *same time*, all over again! The last time was wiped out. I was on a kind of escalator and it carried me up until I reached the place where I realized about what I had to go through, and screamed. And then I was snatched back and put on the bottom again, at the place where the Puerto-Rican driver Senor What's-his-name dumped the gravel and went away again.

And this desert, now. This desert was a sort of landing at the side of the escalator, where I might fall sometimes instead of going all the way to the bottom where the truck came. I had been here before, and I was here again. I had been at the unfinished air base again and again. And there was the other place, with the shining people, and the girl with all those kinds of gold. That was the same place with the crooked moon.

I covered my eyes with my hands and tried to think. The clacking Diesel annoyed me, suddenly, and I got up and reached under the hood and pulled the compression release. Gases chattered out of the ports, and a bubble of silence formed around me, swelling, the last little sounds scampering away from me in all directions, leaving me quiet.

There was a soft thump in the sand beside the machine. It was one of the shining people, the old one, whose forehead was so broad and whose hair was fine, fine like a cobweb. I knew him. I knew his name, too, though I couldn't think of it at the moment.

He dismounted from his flying-chair and came to me.

"Hello," I said. I took my shirt from the seat beside me and hung it on my shoulder. "Come on up."

He smiled and put up his hand. I took it and helped him climb up over the cat. His hands were very strong. He stepped over me and sat down.

"How do you feel?" Sometimes he spoke aloud, and sometimes he didn't, but I always understood him.

"I feel—mixed up."

"Yes, of course," he said kindly. "Go on. Ask me about it."

I looked at him. "Do I—*always* ask you about it?"

"Every time."

"Oh." I looked all around, at the desert, at the hills, at the dozer, at the sun which was too orange. "Where am I?"

"On Earth," he said; only the word he used for Earth meant Earth only to him. It meant *his* earth.

"I know that," I said. "I mean, where am I really? Am I on that air base, or am I here?"

"Oh, you are here," he said.

Somehow I was vastly relieved to hear it. "Maybe you'd better tell me all about it again."

"You said 'again'," he said, and put his hand on my arm. "You're beginning to realize. . . . Good, lad. Good. All right. I'll tell you once more.

"You came here a long time ago. You followed a road with your big noisy machine, and came roaring down out of the desert to the city. The people had never seen a noisy machine before, and they clustered around the gate to see you come. They stood aside to let you pass, and wondered, and you swung the machine and crushed six of them against the gateposts."

"I *did?*" I cried. Then I said. "I did. Oh, I did."

He smiled at me again. "Shh. Don't. It was a long time ago. Shall I go on?

"We couldn't stop you. We have no weapons. We could do nothing in the face of that monster you were driving. You ranged up and down the streets, smashing the fronts of buildings, running people down, and laughing. We had to wait until you got off the machine, and then we overpowered you. You were totally mad. It was," he added thoughtfully, "a very interesting study."

"Why did I do it?" I whispered. "How could I do such things to—*you?*"

"You had been hurt. Dreadfully hurt. You had come here, arriving somewhere near this spot. You were crazed by what you had endured. Later, we followed the tracks of your machine back. We found where you had driven it aimlessly over the desert, and where, once, you had left the machine and lived in a cave, probably for weeks. You ate desert grasses and the eight-legged crabs. You killed everything you could, through some strange, warped revenge motivation.

"You were crazed with thirst and revenge, and you were very thin, and your face was covered with hair, of all extraordinary things, though analysis showed that you had a constant desire for a hairless face. After treatment you became almost rational. But

41

your time-sense was almost totally destroyed. And you had two almost unbreakable psychological blocks—your memory of how you came here, and your sense of identity.

"We did what we could for you, but you were unhappy. The moons had an odd effect on you. We have two, one well inside the other in its orbit, but both with the same period. Without instruments they appear to be an eclipse when they are full. The sight of what you called that crooked moon undid a lot of our work. And then you would get the attacks of an overwhelming emotion you term 'remorse', which appeared to be something like cruelty and something like love and included a partial negation of the will to survive . . . and you could not understand why we would not punish you. Punish you—when you were sick!"

"Yes," I said. "I—remember most of it now. You gave me everything I could want. You even gave me—gave me—"

"Oh—that. Yes. You had some deep-seated convictions about love, and marriage. We felt you would be happier—"

"I was, and then I wasn't. I—I wanted—"

"I know, I know," he said soothingly. "You wanted your name again, and somehow you wanted your own earth."

I clenched my fists until my forearms hurt. "I should be satisfied," I cried. "I should be. You are all so kind, and she—and she— she's been—" I shook my head angrily. "I must be crazy."

"You generally ask me," he said smiling, "at this point, how you came here."

"I do?"

"You do. I'll repeat it. You see, there are irregularities in the fabric of space. No—not space, exactly. We have a word for it—" (he spoke it) "—which means, literally, 'space which is time which is psyche'. It is a condition of space which by its nature creates time and thought and matter. Your world, relative to ours, is in the infinitely great, or in the infinitely small, or perhaps in the infinitely distant, either in space or in time—it does not matter, for they are all the same thing in their ultimate extensions . . . but to go on:

"While you were at your work, you ran your machine into a point of tension in this fabric—a freak, completely improbable position in—" (he spoke the word again) "—in which your universe and ours were tangential. You—went through."

I tensed as he said it.

"Yes, that was the thing. It caused you inconceivable agony. It drove you mad. It filled you full of vengeance and fear. Well, we—cured you of everything but the single fear of going through that agony again, and the peculiar melancholy involving the loss of your ego—your desire to know your own name. Since we failed there—" he shrugged "—we have been doing the only thing left to us. We are trying to send you back."

"Why? Why bother?"

"You are not content here. Our whole social system, our entire philosophy, is based on the contentment of the individual. So we must do what we can . . . in addition, you have given us a tremendous amount of research material in psychology and in theoretical cosmogony. We are grateful. We want you to have what you want. Your fear is great. Your desire is greater. And to help you achieve your desire, we have put you on this course of abre-action."

"Abreaction?"

He nodded. "The psychological re-enactment, or retracing, of everything you have done since you came here, in an effort to return you to the entrance-point in exactly the same frame of mind as that in which you came through it. We cannot find that point. It has something to do with your particular psychic matrix. But if the point is still here, and if, by hypnosis, we can cause you to do exactly what you did when you first came through—why, then, you'll go back."

"Will it be—dangerous?"

"Yes," he said, unhesitatingly. "Even if the point of tangency is still here, where you emerged, it may not be at the same point on your earth. Don't forget—you have been here for eleven of your years. . . . And then there's the agony—bad enough if you do go through, infinitely worse if you do not, for you may drift in—in *somewhere* forever, quite conscious, and with no possibility of release.

"You know all this, and yet you still want us to try. . . ." He sighed. "We admire you deeply, and wonder too; for you are the bravest man we have ever known. We wonder most particularly at your culture, which can produce such an incredible regard for the ego. . . . Shall we try again?"

I looked at the sun which was too orange, and at the hills, and at his broad, quiet, beautiful face. If I could have spoken my name then, I think I should have stayed. If I could have seen *her* just at that moment, I think I should have waited a little longer, at least.

"Yes," I said. "Let's try it again."

I was so afraid that I couldn't remember my name or the name of Gracias de Nada, or something, the fellow who drove the bottom-dump. I couldn't remember how to run the machine; but my hands remembered, and my feet.

Now I sat and looked at the windrow; and then I pulled back the throttle and raised the blade. I swung into the windrow, and the gravel loaded clean on to the blade and cleanly ran off in two even rolls at the sides. When I sensed that the gravel was all off the blade. I stopped, shifted into high reverse, pulled the left steering clutch to me, let in the master clutch, stamped the left brake. . . .

That was the thing, then. Back-blading that roll out—the long small windrow of gravel that had run off the ends of my blade. As I backed over it, the machine straddling it, I dropped the blade on it and floated it, so that it smoothed out the roll. Then it was that I looked back—force of habit, for a bulldozer that size can do real damage backing into powerpoles or buildings—and I saw the muzzy bit of fill.

It was a patch of spread gravel that seemed whirling, blurred at the edges. Look into the sun and then suddenly at the floor. There will be a muzzy patch there whirling and swirling like that. I thought something funny had happened to my eyes. But I didn't stop the machine, and then suddenly I was in it.

Again.

It built up slowly, the agony. It built up in a way that promised more and then carefully fulfilled the promise, and made of the peak of pain a further promise. There was no sense of strain, for everything was poised and counterbalanced and nothing would break. All of the inner force was as strong as all the outer forces, and all of me was the point of equilibrium.

Don't try to think about it. Don't try to imagine for a second. A second of that, unbalanced, would crush you to cosmic dust. There were years of it for me; years and years. . . . I was in an unused stockpile of years, somewhere in a hyperspace, and the weight of them all was on me and in me, consecutively, concurrently.

I woke up very slowly. I hurt all over, and that was an excruciating pleasure, because the pain was only physical.

I began to forget right away.

A company doctor came in and peeped at me. I said, "Hi."

"Well, well," he said, beaming. "So the flying catskinner is with us again."

"What flying catskinner? What happened? Where am I?"

"You're in the dispensary. You, my boy, were working your bulldozer out on the fill and all of a sudden took it into your head to be a flying kay-det at the same time. That's what they say, anyhow. I do know that there wasn't a mark around the machine where it lay—not for sixty feet. You sure didn't drive it over there."

"What are you talking about?"

"That, son, I wouldn't know. But I went and looked myself. There lay the Cat, all broken up, and you beside it with your lungs all full of your own ribs. Deadest looking man I ever saw get better."

"I don't get it. Did anybody see this happen? Are you trying to—"

"Only one claims to have seen it was a Puerto-Rican bottom-dump driver. Doesn't speak any English, but he swears on every saint in the calendar that he looked back after dumping a load and

44

saw you and twenty tons of bulldozer *forty feet in the air*, and then it was coming down!"

I stared. "Who was the man?"

"Heavy-set fellow. About forty-five. Strong as a rhino and seemed sane."

"I know him," I said. "A good man." Suddenly, then, happily: "Doc—you know what his name is?"

"No. Didn't ask. Some flowery Spanish moniker, I guess."

"No, it isn't," I said. "His name is Kirkpatrick. Alonzo Padin de Kirkpatrick."

He laughed. "The Irish are a wonderful people. Go to sleep. You've been unconscious for nearly three weeks."

"I've been unconscious for eleven years," I said, and felt foolish as hell because I hadn't meant to say anything like that and couldn't imagine what put it into my head.

THE PIPER

BY RAY BRADBURY

> To a great many people Modern Science Fiction begins and
> ends with *Ray Bradbury.* The remarkable creator of modern
> classics like "The Martian Chronicles" and "Something
> Wicked This Way Comes" has a style which rings like poetry,
> expressing ordinary—and extraordinary—things in a way that
> is totally unique. Bradbury's rise to the position of eminence
> which he now enjoys was not easy, however. His early writings
> often display his influences too openly and his desperate search
> for publication frequently made him compromise his own
> natural flair simply to see his work in print. But thanks to a
> shrewd agent and one or two adventurous editors, the young
> Bradbury was encouraged to let the torrent of words locked in
> him spill out onto the page. "The Piper" which appears here
> was the first story he wrote without a collaborator—he had
> co-authored a number of prior tales with an established S.F.
> writer, Henry Hasse—and it has stood the passage of time well.
> Enthusiasts of Bradbury's work will see in it shades of what
> was to follow in "The Martian Chronicles"—to those who
> have not read this great work it will serve as a worthy in-
> troduction.

From space, Mars was like a copper-coloured lantern, burning
feebly, growing old, and dying. It resembled a large blossom as
the Jovian space-ship approached it.

Kerac, the Martian, stood in the heart of his ship, watching the
lovely, faded flower unfold like the soft petals of memory—half
afraid to look, not quite knowing what changes twenty years
might have brought to his homeland. Mars, at first glance, was the
same. Fingers of nostalgia touched him. Strange tears stung his
eyes. But as the ship needled down through lean atmosphere, the
physiognomy of the planet appeared scarred. Sprawling over the
Martian meadowland lay a city, its pattern of black and white
splotches merging into a bulging idiot eye. "Jovian riff-raff",
swore Kerac as he peered downward. "What a mess!"

His thin fingers tightened, his spidery hands clutching a silver
musical Pipe upon which he had composed his symphonies and
folk-tunes—his only link with his past, with his fame as a composer
and musician.

Kerac began to shiver as if a quiet wind were blowing through him—a wind of resentment and fear and a strange deep anger. The city's lines emerged in sharper detail. It was filthily unplanned, a proof of decay rather than progress. There was no questioning of fact that this city had been thrown together by the awkward, drunken hand of the Jovian colonizers. Squalor and the character of these pale-blue creatures from Jupiter were synonymous.

Highways shot out from the core of the city, throwing tentacles of metal southward to three other Jovian cities; each as disproportioned and irritating to the eye as the first.

Kerac raged, half to himself, half to the short, flabby, blue-skinned Jovian who stood with slitted dark eyes beside him.

"Look what they've done!" he cried. "For a million years that valley was green and fertile, soft with growing things. They've torn it up, hunting for minerals! Those mountains in the South—they were regular and beautiful. They've ripped the tops off them and shattered the sides! Is *this* your blue-print for the colonization of Mars? Is this what I must enjoy on my return from exile?"

Kerac fell silent. The blue-skinned Jovian, mute and small in comparison with the incredibly tall and thin musician said nothing.

The exile's face was a fine network of lines. A dry, brown, bird-like face it was, aquiline and keen-eyed. There was about him an indefinable air of mystery and melancholy. And now he was looking down into the faces of ten million dead Martians. They cried out to him for only one thing. They asked revenge. That was all.

"There," said Kerac, pointing. "See where the river flows down from the hills?"

The Jovian compressed his thick lips, said nothing. The exile continued.

"I was born near the mouth of that stream, up that way, where the mountains are purple. Look at it now! Marred by twenty years of smoke, grime and filth, and now turned into a sewage canal!"

"The Klondike days on Earth were as bad," snapped the Jovian, speaking for the first time in minutes. "This is the same rush on a larger scale. The end justifies the means!"

The small Jovian projectile nosed the soil, rocking to rest. Ports slid open. Seconds later, Kerac walked on Martian soil for the first time in twenty years. It was the same spongy, moist-smelling ground that his childish feet had skipped on, but now it was littered with trash, scarred and slashed by the jets of space-ships, blotched with machine oil.

Kerac stood looking a moment. Audio pillars, situated at various points about the landing field spilled music, garish Jovian songs of dissonance and chaos. Then, with an oath, Kerac kicked. A discarded *utana* bottle went ricochetting noisily.

They left the rocket-port, walked into the town, into narrow,

47

alley-like streets, filled with the thick, fishy odour of Jovian food. Laughter echoed down crooked-spined thoroughfares. Glasses shattered. Now and then a gun snapped, propelling death, adding to the din of the alien city. The Jovian indicated a shabby dwelling.

"Sleep there."

"Thank you, no." Kerac spun on one heel, walked off toward the edge of town where the stream wound past on its way from the violet-tinged hills. "I'm going where I can breathe."

The Jovian made no move to follow, but grunted, "The Council will jail you if you do not report once a day. I will expect you tomorrow, Martian!"

"If you want me, just follow the stream—" Kerac's voice faded like a bird flying into the gathering twilight.

He walked quickly, his jaw tightened. Misery was in his soul. The harsh lights burnt his eyes. The music of Jupiter poured from towering audios all over the town, constant, grating. And, once, faintly, the sound of giggling women cut in his ears.

The sun was setting as he reached the quiet stream. He knelt there with the water lapping at his knees and prayed to the stars that some plan would help him end all this.

The stream was cold to his fingers, as cold as the blood of the Martian race which had committed suicide in order not to be engulfed and controlled by the tide of colonials swarming from Jupiter. Kerac thought of the pioneers, of his murdered family, the desecrated soil. He prayed even more fervently.

"Kam, give me strength," he asked. "Kam, give me strength."

When the city was left sprawled behind him, he walked with a new spring to his legs. Exhilaration poured through him, a song came to his lips. He lifted his silver Pipe and played his song to the hills. The hills repeated it, softly.

Stars came out, the stream at his side murmured melodies as it flowed over pebbles. Suddenly time was no obstacle. Time flew back. Twenty years fell away like a misted veil. Everything was peaceful again. There was no conquest, nothing but beauty and the night.

He turned to look at the Jovian city and its lights, a million-eyed monster defacing the plain. Other music interrupted the song on his lips. Music from the audios in the city, broadcast so loudly that the East wind plucked it, carried it to the hills.

Kerac restrained a curse, and plunged on. The mad music tagged at his heels. Was there no escaping them?

The wind changed. The music of Jove died into silence. He sighed with relief. It would not be long, he thought. He had come home to die. He was old. The Jovian scientists had finished dissecting him physically and psychologically, and now were sending him to his dead planet, knowing full well that alone he could not harm them. He was the last of the Golden Race.

But what of the Creatures in the Martian mountains, the vast unnamable hordes of amorphous, guttural-voiced entities that inhabited the caves of Mars? Had they been as ruthlessly wiped out as the great Golden Race?

The Dark Race had not committed suicide, this much Kerac knew. And it would have taken time to clean them all out of the million caves. A faint spark of hope began to flicker within him.

Looking out over a dimly illuminated stretch of desert in one direction, the lifeless Martian city of Kam lay desolate. Kam's aged spires towered toward thin air, flinging out great symmetrically designed parkways and gardens like the unused pinions of a magnificent bird, for ever quiescent, no more to live, no more to fly.

Not long ago that city had breathed, given birth to millions of Martians, swaddled them, raised them, given them riches, happiness from untold centuries of idyllic existence.

Kerac caressed his musical Pipe, the instrument that had given him solace during his long exile on Jupiter.

He gazed idly. A great swarm of creatures flew up from the dead city of Kam—a trail of soaring white birds crossing stars with a shrill song in their thousand throats. Repeating and repeating their song, again and again, fading, fading and fading still more, until only a vestige of an echo wandered back in a soft finale.

Away they flew over the synthetic Jovian streets and down over the horizon from which would come the rising sun many hours later.

Then a deep grumble reached Kerac's ears. The grumble had started even as the great Kam birds flapped high with their waning song, had reached a peak as the birds subsided into the far lands. Now the grumble began to fade, but not before Kerac realized what it was.

When the birds came, singing, the grumbling followed close. But the dull grumble came from the ground, from the dim caverns of the mountains. And he knew what caused the grumble—The Dark Race! Deep in the caves they still survived. Elation flamed within him. Martians still existed, even if they were the dull-brained, mis-shaped Dark Race. Kerac had an ally!

Kerac had no plan as he approached the caverns of the Dark Race. He walked slowly between sheer walls that stretched five hundred feet skyward as through granite slabs of a tomb city. All was velvet silence, and only his feet beat a gentle scuff-scuff on the rock.

He stopped, touched with excitement yet a dash of fear. Something rustled just ahead. A dark shape manifested itself. Greenish eyes glared at Kerac. A low guttural snarl came through the gloom.

The shape moved sluggishly, like a ponderous, semi-human amoeba; a mass of ebon life on the verge of imitating Man. It reared up on thick black legs, groping out with fat dark arms and thick, hungry fingers. It opened a wide, lipless mouth and grunted.

Kerac fell back, fear tightening his chest like a vice. His fingers sought his silver musical Pipe. But he didn't carry it to his lips. What good was music against this terror?

He attempted an appeal to the creature.

"My friend," he appealed softly. "We are brothers. We have been blasphemed by the men from another star."

He paused, then repeated: "We are brothers."

The unhuman thing swayed. The two legs slobbered on firm rock in a horrible imitation of walking. A semblance of an arm writhed out in Kerac's direction.

"Will you help me?" pleaded Kerac. "The beasts of Jove are tearing at you. They take your riches, defile the veldtlands. Soon they come here to wipe you out. But before they do, help me."

The creature snarled and turned. From the caves a dozen voices shrieked reply. Karac retreated six paces.

"We are brothers, don't you understand? We have a duty, a task to perform. Help me to act now."

A roaring wall of voices rushed from the deep caves. Overhead, a cloudlet of Kam birds wafted by, singing. And with their appearance, the Dark Race gave birth to a volcano of ear-shattering cries. Hundreds of them floundered, groped, stumbled, reeled out of the stuffy tunnels.

Kerac whipped about as a thousand green eyes stared at him. His heart churned defeat and anger and hopelessness. They started to close in. He fled.

He ran until he reached a place where the walls broadened out. Here he paused. The Dark Race came no further. They had never advanced beyond this boundary. Never. Only their voices, cold, pestilential, menacing, had transcended.

Even now they gave up the brief chase, returned to their caves. The night became as quiet as the distant pin-point stars. Jupiter gloated in the heaven.

Kerac, with weary feet, returned to the city of Jove, retracing his path along the glittering stream; his posture, his every step, word and thought, one of deepest despair. . . .

"Hoa!"

Kerac continued walking in the narrow alley.

"Hoa! You!" A Jovian, immense and long-armed, staggered out from the bright scarlet light of a *utana* den.

Kerac walked on.

"Hoa!"

The man snatched at Kerac, twisted him about and sent him sprawling to the street.

"When I speak, you listen," growled the man. He was huge, bloated and odorous with the smell of *oama*-weed and the brain-bruising *utana* liquor.

Kerac tried to gain his feet, but the man's heavy boot thrust him back. The purple face grimaced.

"You the Martian?"

Jerac nodded to save himself another jolt from the poised boot.

"I thought so." The Jovian laughed drunkenly. "Now, Martian, you will entertain. You will oblige me."

Kerac blinked at the Jovian. A crowd was gathering. The Jovian turned to the throng.

"He is the Martian, the musician you heard about."

A murmur passed through the gathering. Someone said, "So that is a Martian? By the teeth of Jobar, he is brittle."

The first Jovian went on, after swallowing a mouthful of *utana* from a hand-flask. "This musician will play for us. Take him inside."

A hand pushed him. Kerac stumbled up, protesting. A fist lashed out, swiping across his lips. Fingers gripped him tight. Hot, sweating bodies pressed him into the *utana* hut that was blazing with painfully bright scarlet lamps and thick with the haze of burning *oama* cigarettes.

The walls were painted a hideous yellow and the ceiling was low and garish with a hundred different nightmare designs—the effect on the whole producing a sense of drunkenness in a person almost immediately.

"Sit here." The Jovian leader picked Kerac up by his collar and shoved him into a low chair. "Now," he said, pointing, "play."

Kerac found himself confronted by a wierd, intricate Jovian musical instrument, somewhat like an insane version of an ancient organ.

Kerac shrugged helplessly. "I can't. I don't know how."

The huge Jovian scowled. "When I, Brondar, command someone to play—"

"He is flat," someone cut in shrilly. "Give him the weed to smoke. Give him *utana* to drink."

"Ua! Ua!" the others assented thickly.

Brondar turned. "Give him dreams, Nar. I will pay."

Nar produced a flagon of *utana* quickly, offering it to Kerac, who refused it.

Nar, an abnormally short, under-nourished Jovian, leered. His blue skull-like face worked.

"You refuse?"

"I do not drink."

"You do not drink! Martian, when Nar produces *utana* he expects that person to drink." The glass was poked against Kerac's lips. "Now, drink. Else you eat the glass."

Kerac's lips became a tight, firm line. His whole body shook

51

with resentment.

"Drink it," roared the man named Brondar.

Nar was angered. He pulled back his arm and sloshed the liquor over Kerac's face. The crowd roared approval. Nar stomped off to his *utana* cubicle, leaving the Martian to splutter and swab his face dry with his cape.

"Now," commanded Brondar, "will you play? Or will we be forced to—"

Kerac controlled himself. Quietly he reached into his cloak, brought out his Pipe. "I can only play this," he said.

"What?" came the roar. "A Pipe?"

"Ua! Ua!" the others drowned Brondar out. "Let him play. Let us hear."

Brondar scowled mightily. Finally he seated himself at a low table and roared, "Play".

Kerac played. He played until he was fatigued, haggard. Again and again they made him perform. And once, Brondar fired an electro-pistol at Kerac's feet, making him dance and play simultaneously.

Not before the dawn lifted in the east did he finally rest. The smoke den was practically empty. The butts of *oama* weed littered the floor. Jovians crumpled in corners, snored. Nar was draped over the *utana* cubicle's railing, and Brondar, still torpidly active, hiccuped and spat oaths at the wild-coloured ceiling.

It was then that a flotilla of Kam birds winged from over the mountains, over the Jovian city and toward the rising sun. They sang their song, high, sweet, insistent. Immediately there came a faint, answering grumble.

Kerac received his first inspiration, his first clue. He listened. His Pipe clattered to the floor. Stooping to pick it up, he stopped, looked strangely at it lying there, his eyes widening. Then he looked to Brondar, who was stirring, mumbling in a husky voice.

"Whass that?" asked Brondar. "That noise?"

"The birds," murmured Nar. "The Kam birds."

"Au. Au." Brondar shook a woozey head. "I mean the *other* noise, the other noise."

"Marsquake," said Nar, feebly rousing himself. "Shifting strata in the hills."

Kerac jerked up, the Pipe in his hands, and ideas sprouting full-bloomed in his brain. These ignorant Jovians didn't even *know* the Dark Race lived in the mountains.

And Kam birds. They became part of a colossal plan that had suddenly exploded inside Kerac.

Brondar swayed, rose, his purpled face retching. "Oa. Where are you going, Martian?"

Brondar barred the way to the door.

In desperation Kerac seized upon an empty *utana* jug and

crashed it full on Brondar's skull.

Brondar ceased barring the way.

The painted signs had not been evident at night, when Kerac had first passed this way, but they were posted every hundred yards, their black letters hot under the morning sun:

DANGER!
MARSQUAKES
SHIFTING OF STRATA

In smaller letters he read: "Any employee of Jovian Minerals discovered beyond this point will be dismissed immediately."

Kerac stood there for a long moment, the sun slashing at his tall body. The hills were not far off, baked in the oven of the early hours. The stream glittered like a million flashing knife blades. He tried to piece together the jigsaw of the signs and the ignorance in the Jovian city.

The Dark Race had survived in the mountains, untouched. The Jovian labourers called the noise that came from the mountains, "Marsquakes." There was only one possible explanation. A big job of excavating was going on in the South. The Southern mountains were already vacuumed clean of the Dark Race. These Northern ranges would be flushed soon, when the Jovians were ready to begin work here.

Until that time, the officials had decided that what the ordinary labourer didn't know wouldn't hurt him. So the Dark Race was kept secret. If the workers knew about the menace, many of them would have quit immediately. They were a superstitious lot—these Jovians.

Anyway, the Dark Race was no real menace. They didn't have the brains to organize and attack. They killed themselves. Even an intelligent man like Kerac would be unable to organize them. The Jovian Council knew this or they would never have allowed Kerac to return.

Kerac hurried on in the blistering warmth.

On the mountain top it was cooler. From where he stood he could command a view of both cities; the ancient and the modern. Off in the South came the noises of busy excavators in the Yellow Mountains.

He waited patiently until the Kam birds flew over the caverns, drawing forth a trembling Marsquake response.

When the birds vanished, Kerac, with a confident smile, lifted his Pipe and played the very same notes that the birds had flung from the sky—ten notes, short, plaintive. Followed by six long sweet chords, and then lower and more insistent notes—an urgent summons. Over and over again, piping to the night wind.

The mountains took up the song. But it was as weak as the last faint dawn star.

The Dark Race responded, quivering the earth. But Kerac knew they would not venture into the hated sun.

They heard his song and were stimulated by it. This much was optimistic. He would practise, listen to the Kam birds again and again, impressing their melody on his brain, making his interpretation of it more expressive, more urgent. And then, when night came. . . .

At twilight Kerac stationed himself nearer the mountain base. He played the music, offered it to the slight wind that wafted down through the slate-grey walls to the holes where the creatures squatted glaring at him.

The music was heard by the creatures, coerced them. They came plodding out, their feet moist on the rocks, gesticulating ponderously, uttering cyclopean grunts.

Kerac ran to take another station. The creatures swarmed slowly out, hypnotized by the breeze-borne melody, over the narrow gullies, down the small cliffs.

"Come, my brothers," shouted Kerac wildly. "Come. Kill the Jovians." He played the hellish music. It arrowed to the stars and shook them in their orbits.

Down into the sloping foothills Kerac moved, cautiously, the inflamed horde following his music. And then a great, shattering wind came from the Jovian city, bearing with it another music. The Jovian music, the maddening symphony of sound that ravened the air.

It devoured Kerac's pitifully weak song, punched fists of noise at the Dark Beasts and sent them whimpering, fleeing, back to the caves, back into the mountains, back into the Stygian gloom.

Kerac, struck mute, defeated, stood with the hideous Jovian music consuming the air he breathed. The music, spawned through the towering audios in the city, thrived on the east wind, flung up echoes, demanded attention. Demanded it and received it.

Kerac put his Pipe away, his lean face hieroglyphed with defeat. His last hope, his last plan destroyed by the wind from the east and the music of Jove.

He stood there a moment, with the wind fondling his cloak, tossing dust into his face.

The wind.

The wind!

Kerac turned about, exhilarated at this new breeze-inspired solution. He ran, bounding from rock to rock, fighting the wind, returning to Jove City for the last time.

Kerac hurried through narrow streets, musing over his task. It could not be accomplished with direct, drastic action. It would take a peaceful, psychological bit of handling that would throw no suspicion upon himself until it was too late.

A ponderous twenty-wheeled ore-vehicle hissed to a halt in the street. A beefy Jovian mountain leaped down, bawling loudly: "Hoa, Martian."

It was Brondar, returning from the work in the Southern mountains. But he was smiling.

His huge blue arm shot out, picked Kerac up by his blouse. "I have been looking for you since you ran this morning. I have need of you and your Pipe. Come."

He stalked off, dragging Kerac after him through the rambling alleyway.

"Release me," demanded Kerac angrily. "I'm a charge of the Jovian government."

"Charge?" A tremendous snorting laugh wrinkled the bruised-blue face. "Government? There is no government here. Walk." And he shoved Kerac ahead of him through the semi-gloom.

"We will make money together, Martian," he said. "After you ran this morning, the audio base official came to the *utana* den. I told him of your music. He is interested. He is looking for a man such as you. Now I have found you again, and I will demand that the audio official pay me well for discovering you and your Pipe! Turn here."

Kerac was thrust around a corner into a plaza at the centre of which stood a yellowish building with the word AUDIO printed in large Jovian scrawl above the roof.

Up the steps and through a door they went. Inside, six Jovians sat about a table conferring; bottles of *utana* at every elbow, *oama* cigarettes in every cobalt-lipped mouth. Ugly faces turned towards him. He realized, by the insignia on their bulging uniforms, that these men were the highest officials in the local government. These were some of the men responsible for the destruction of Mars.

The man heading the table jumped up. "Brondar," he clipped. "You interrupt conference. What is it?"

Brondar shoved Kerac forward, waved a big paw to the assemblage and said, "He did not escape, Grannd. He will play music for you, as I promised. And you will pay me well for finding him."

Grannd, the short Jovian, came quickly to Kerac, his little dark eyes flicking over the tall Martian's cloaked form.

"You are the Martian." It was a statement. "I have heard of you from Jupiter when you were exiled. There you did as you pleased. Here, where there is less law and more prejudice, you will act as we please. They say you are good. I, Grannd, will judge. Play."

Kerac looked at Grannd, knowing that here was the head of the

55

audio base, the building from which all broadcasts emanated over the city through the audio pillars.

Now, if Kerac played his cards right, the Jovians would co-operate in their own destruction.

The next few minutes would be crucial, the next hour would mean either the success or failure of his whole plan. He was a little frightened because his big opportunity had arrived so soon.

Kerac seated himself, pretending to be sullen, procured his Pipe and set about producing music.

The music was so low and so sad and so sweet that the *oama* smoke ceased idling in the room and froze upon the air.

The Jovian officials, posed in various slit-eyed postures over their *oama* and *utana*, found themselves clutched in the vice of enchantment. This was musical hypnotics. Each note touched ears that ached for more. It was the melancholy song of the Kam birds, slower and sadder than ever it had been interpreted.

When Kerac finished, he played it over because the silence that followed could not be assimilated by the nerves. He played it over, a little faster. The room was quiet. Even Brondar, impressed, did not speak.

Finishing the second time, Kerac was greeted with no applause. There are wondrous things in the universe that one does not appreciate with noise, but with reverent silence. It would have been like crying "Bravo!" in the midst of a majestic church mass, or clapping hands at a glimpse of an awesome spiral nebula.

Then there was silence.

Brondar stirred uneasily, as if he had appreciated beauty for the first time in his life and was resentful because of it. Finally he swore and lighted an *oama* cigarette.

The five officials came out of their trance, murmured among themselves uneasily, smoked, lifted and emptied their flagons of liquor.

Grannd sipped his *utana*, thinking. He turned to the officials. The officials nodded. Grannd turned to Kerac.

"You will repeat that, so I can make an audio transcription of it."

Kerac repressed the smile that came to his lips. Grannd continued to talk.

"You did well. You should be flattered that I, Grannd, have said so." His speech was clipped as short as his stature. Conceit oozed from the man. He expected a "thank you" instantly.

Kerac mused, taking his time purposely. He did not wish to seem eager to co-operate.

"I don't know," he replied slowly. "I have always refused, before, to record."

Grannd's eyes crackled. "But you will. For me. Now. Immediately."

"Why?"

56

"Why?" Grannd puffed out blue cheeks. "I, Grannd, will transmit your music to Jupiter, present it through audio pillars all over Mars. Perhaps to Earth. You will write a symphony. It will be profitable." His voice was hard. "Come. We will make sound tests. If they are acceptable, we will sign contracts."

Grannd started for a door that led into a soundproofed room, expected that Kerac was following. Kerac was not.

Brondar had to use force.

Kerac stood before a series of intricate acoustical instruments. Grannd cursed over a maze of machinery in the recording booth. The Jovian officials sat in a glassed cubicle, watching. Brondar with visions of much money, stood by.

A small sound-spool was adjusted. Grannd looked up. "When I signal, you play. You are ready? Silence, then."

A pause. Then, the signal.

Kerac played as he had never played before. He played the song slowly, and then, with each time he repeated it, he went faster, faster, higher, shriller. He played it eight times, becoming more insistent. And on the eighth rendition inaudible. But it was grimly, terribly commanding.

"Good!" Grannd snapped off the sound-spool transcriber. "You are talented. This will bring much money."

Kerac was amused. "What is it that you find in my music that interests you so?"

"Interests?" The radioman patted his chest. "It does something to me—here."

"But will the others like it—the labourers?"

"You have seen what it does to the men who drink *utana* and smoke *oama*. If they like, everyone will like it."

"I'm sceptical. I don't believe it."

This irked Grannd tremendously ."I will prove it." He snatched up the sound-spool, transferred it to another machine, made dial adjustments and said, "We have audio pillars in every street of the city."

"Yes. I noticed them several times."

"I will transmit your music through those audios immediately, proving that you are talented by offering you to the labourers, to everyone."

"And don't forget," Brondar put in, "*I* discovered him."

Grannd snapped a button, the sound-spool turned. "If you wish," he said, "you can step outside and listen to this over the street audios."

Kerac nodded and headed for the door with Brondar behind him. In the night air, he paused, smiling. He turned to Brondar. "Shall we go to the *utana* den to listen?" he asked.

Brondar laughed, nodded.

Kerac felt the breeze plucking at his cloak. "Good. Good," he said, as they started walking. "There is a strong wind from the east tonight. A wind from the east."

This night the music was different when it spilled from the audios. It was the same music Kerac had played faintly in the hills, but now it was monstrously amplified. It came from Jove City, the east wind seized upon it, shoved it over the hills like a scourge of locusts and let it fall in a vast curtain of hypnotism into the dark caverns.

In five minutes the trails, the gullies, the hills and mountaintops were alive with a creeping, ever-changing line of amoeba-like figures that swarmed down in a huge tide. The tide crossed the river, slobbered along the highway, summoned by the music.

The Dark Race was not alone in the spell. Every Jovian in the city stood frozen, listening to the wondrous beauty of music.

The marsquake moved through the hills with increasing noise. The music screamed higher and higher, faster and faster, insane, sending shock after shock through night air.

Kerac stood near the back entrance of the *utana* den, Brondar at his side. The marsquake ceased as the Dark Race approached, some psychic sense causing them to silence themselves.

The whole city was inanimate except for the sudden rushing slobber of alien feet in the narrow alleys on the edge of town.

Kerac waited, ready to escape at a moment's notice.

Nar, the proprietor of the smoke-den, was busy filling a flagon with *utana*, listening in a trance to the music and the sound from the hills. "Marsquake," he growled.

The door to the smoke den slammed open. In the doorway loomed dark shapeless entities with green eyes. There was a period of electric unbelief. In that instant Kerac slipped out the back entrance quietly.

Nar looked up from his flagons, his blue brow furrowed. "Oa!" he cried angrily. "What is this?"

Three tables overturned. Six blue hands reached for guns. Two men fainted. Twenty flagons hit the floor, rolling in crazy circles, spilling *utana* over the boards. Brondar pulled his electro-pistol and fired.

The Dark Creatures came in to meet the bullets. Bullets do no good in black pulp. The electro-pistols had no effect. The creatures slobbered forward, unhurt. They were hungry, famished.

They took what they wanted.

Kerac, running, turned off into a side alley and waited, catching his breath. Squatting down, panting and sweating with exertion, a great calmness blessed him. The agitation was gone, the fear was gone. He felt a little drunk with power. Next he would go to the other Jovian cities, in the vast blue depths of the valleys on the other side of Mars.

Faintly, on a ripple of wind, came voices—an army of screams ripping through cool air. The screams climbed up over the city. Shots echoed. Thousands of them. Muffled footsteps pattered through the alley near him. Back against the wall Kerac realized his escape was cut off. Somehow he was not afraid. He had finished his work. There was no stopping the Dark Race now. They would carry on without him.

Stumbling Jovians ran wailing past him. They met a wave pouring down the street. They stopped a little beyond where Kerac lay, and were embraced, crushed, silenced by a score of the Dark Things!

Kerac leaned back, took his Pipe and laid it against his lips.

Stars shone in his eyes, triumphant.

Life in this gigantic octopus city was dying. The tentacles were withering, one by one, the giant yellow eyes were winking, fading, going out, leaving blackness. Even the music was killed by the black tidal wave.

Kerac carried on with the music until he felt the dark bodies pressing near him, the thick hungry fingers snatching at the Pipe, at his cloak, at his throat . . .

COLUMBUS WAS A DOPE

BY ROBERT HEINLEIN

Three times winner of the coveted Hugo Award, *Robert Heinlein* is widely regarded as a spokesman for the younger generation—a writer who displays in his work not only a deep understanding of the world's problems but has his own very special interpretations to put on them. His early life was spent in the U.S. Navy—until he was invalided out—and this has proved a major influence on his work. But for all his success in recent years, Heinlein has constantly suffered from unsympathetic publishers, bad reviews and countless imitators "lifting" his best ideas. Nevertheless his unique blend of humour (seen at its best in this choise early item), controversy and storytelling power make him one of the most revered of all modern writers.

"I do like to wet down a sale," the fat man said happily, raising his voice above the sighing of the air-conditioner. "Drink up, Professor, I'm two ahead of you."

He glanced up from their table as the elevator door opposite them opened. A man stepped out into the cool dark of the bar and stood blinking, as if he had just come from the desert glare outside.

"Hey, Fred—Fred Nolan," the fat man called out. "Come over!" He turned to his guest. "Man I met on the hop from New York. Siddown, Fred. Shake hands with Professor Appleby, Chief Engineer of the Starship *Pegasus*—or will be when she's built. I just sold the Professor an order of bum steel for his crate. Have a drink on it."

"Glad to, Mr. Barnes," Nolan agreed. "I've met Dr. Appleby. On business—Climax Instrument Company."

"Huh?"

"Climax is supplying us with precision equipment," offered Appleby.

Barnes looked surprised, then grinned. "That's one on me. I took Fred for a government man, or one of you scientific johnnies. What'll it be, Fred? Old-fashioned? The same Professor?"

"Right. But please don't call me 'Professor'. I'm not one and it ages me. I'm still young."

"I'll say you are, uh—Doc. Pete! Two old-fashioneds and another double Manhattan! I guess I expected a comic book

60

scientist, with a long white beard. But now that I've met you, I can't figure out one thing."

"Which is?"

"Well, at your age you bury yourself in this god-forsaken place—"

"We couldn't build the *Pegasus* on Long Island," Appleby pointed out, "and this is the ideal spot for the take off."

"Yeah, sure, but that's not it. It's—well, mind you, I sell steel. You want special alloys for a starship; I sell it to you. But just the same, now that business is out of the way, why do you want to do it? Why try to go to Proxima Centauri, or any other star?"

Appleby looked amused. "It can't be explained. Why do men try to climb Mount Everest? What took Peary to the North Pole? Why did Columbus get the Queen to hock her jewels? Nobody has ever been to Proxima Centauri—so we're going."

Barnes turned to Nolan. "Do you get it, Fred?"

Nolan shrugged. "I sell precision instruments. Some people raise chrysanthemums; some build starships. I sell instruments."

Barnes' friendly face looked puzzled. "Well—" The bartender put down their drinks. "Say, Pete, tell me something. Would you go along on the *Pegasus* expedition if you could?"

"Nope."

"Why not?"

"I like it here."

Dr. Appleby nodded. "There's your answer, Barnes, in reverse. Some have the Columbus spirit and some haven't."

"It's all very well to talk about Columbus," Barnes persisted, "but he expected to come back. You guys don't expect to. Sixty years—you told me it would take sixty years. Why, you may not even live to get there."

"No, but our children will. And our grandchildren will come back."

"But—Say, you're not *married*?"

"Certainly I am. Family men only on the expedition. It's a two-to-three generation job. You know that." He hauled out a wallet. "There's Mrs. Appleby, with Diane. Diane is three and a half."

"She's a pretty baby," Barnes said soberly and passed it on to Nolan, who smiled at it and handed it back to Appleby. Barnes went on "What happens to her?"

"She goes with us, naturally. You wouldn't want her put in an orphanage, would you?"

"No, but—" Barnes tossed off the rest of his drink. "I don't get it," he admitted. "Who'll have another drink?"

"Not for me, thanks," Appleby declined, finishing his more slowly and standing up. "I'm due home. Family man, you know." He smiled.

Barnes did not try to stop him. He said goodnight and watched Appleby leave.

"My round," said Nolan. "The same?"

"Huh? Yeah, sure." Barnes stood up. "Let's get up to the bar, Fred, where we can drink properly. I need about six."

"Okay," Nolan agreed, standing up. "What's the trouble?"

"Trouble? Did you see that picture?"

"Well?"

"Well, how do *you* feel about it? I'm a salesman, too, Fred. I sell steel. It don't matter what the customer wants to use it for; I sell it to him. I'd sell a man a rope to hang himself. But I do love kids. I can't stand to think of that cute little kid going along on that— that crazy expedition!"

"Why not? She's better off with her parents. She'll get as used to steel decks as most kids are to sidewalks."

"But look, Fred. You don't have any silly idea they'll make it, do you?"

"They might."

"Well, they won't. They don't stand a chance. I *know*. I talked it over with our technical staff before I left the home office. Nine chances out of ten they'll burn up on the take off. That's the best that can happen to them. If they get out of the solar system, which ain't likely, they'll still never make it. They'll never reach the stars."

Pete put another drink down in front of Barnes. He drained it and said:

"Set up another one, Pete. They can't. It's a theoretical impossibility. They'll freeze—or they'll roast—or they'll starve. But they'll never get there."

"Maybe so."

"No maybe about it. They're *crazy*. Hurry up with that drink, Pete. Have one yourself."

"Coming up. Don't mind if I do, thanks." Pete mixed the cocktail, drew a glass of beer, and joined them.

"Pete, here, is a wise man," Barnes said confidently. "You don't catch him monkeying around with any trips to the stars. Columbus —Pfui! Columbus was a dope. He shoulda stayed in bed."

The bartender shook his head. "You got me wrong, Mr. Barnes. If it wasn't for men like Columbus, we wouldn't be here today— now, would we? I'm just not the explorer type. But I'm a believer. I got nothing against the *Pegasus* expedition."

"You don't approve of them taking kids on it, do you?"

"Well . . . there were kids on the *Mayflower*, so they tell mè."

"It's not the same thing." Barnes looked at Nolan, then back to the bartender. "If the Lord had intended us to go to the stars, he would have equipped us with jet propulsion. Fix me another drink, Pete."

"You've had about enough for a while, Mr. Barnes."

The troubled fat man seemed about to argue, thought better of it.

"I'm going up to the Sky Room and find somebody that'll dance with me," he announced. "G'night." He swayed softly toward the elevator.

Nolan watched him leave. "Poor old Barnes." He shrugged. "I guess you and I are hard-hearted, Pete."

"No. I believe in progress, that's all. I remember my old man wanted a law passed about flying machines, keep 'em from breaking their fool necks. Claimed nobody ever could fly, and the government should put a stop to it. He was wrong. I'm not the adventurous type myself but I've seen enough people to know they'll try anything once, and that's how progress is made."

"You don't look old enough to remember when men couldn't fly."

"I've been around a long time. Ten years in this one spot."

"Ten years, eh? Don't you ever get a hankering for a job that'll let you breathe a little fresh air?"

"Nope. I didn't get any fresh air when I served drinks on Forty-second Street and I don't miss it now. I like it here. Always something new going on here, first the atom laboratories and then the big observatory and now the Starship. But that's not the real reason. I like it here. It's my home. Watch this."

He picked up a brandy inhaler, a great fragile crystal globe, spun it and threw it, straight up, toward the ceiling. It rose slowly and gracefully, paused for a long reluctant wait at the top of its rise, then settled slowly, slowly, like a diver in a slow-motion movie. Pete watched it float past his nose, then reached out with thumb and forefinger, nipped it easily by the stem, and returned it to the rack.

"See that," he said. "One-sixth gravity. When I was tending bar on earth my bunions gave me the dickens all the time. Here I weigh only thirty-five pounds. I like it on the Moon."

CASTAWAY

ARTHUR C. CLARKE

Discovering a story by *Arthur C. Clarke* which has not previously been anthologised or published in a collection of the
author's works is almost like looking for a needle in a hay-
stack. For Mr. Clarke has never been a prodigious writer and
each new story has invariably quickly found its way between
book covers. The secret behind this tale which appears here in
volume form for the first time is that it was published in a small,
ill-fated S.F. magazine called "Fantasy" under the pen-name
of Charles Willis. Like his counterpart across the Atlantic,
Isaac Asimov, Clarke has a deep interest in, and knowledge of,
science and some of his earliest writings just before the out-
break of World War II were on purely scientific topics such as
the planets and space flight. In recent years, however, because
of the scope of his work he has found magazines as varied as
"Playboy", "Vogue" and "Reader's Digest" more than
eager to publish him. In many ways he has played a major part
in bringing dignity and authority to a genre too often dismissed
as being merely the haunt of "rocket ships and bug-eyed
monsters".

"Most of the matter in the universe is at temperatures so high
that no chemical compounds can exist, and the atoms themselves are stripped of all but their inner electron screens. Only
on those incredibly rare bodies known as planets can the
familiar elements and their combinations exist and, in all still
rarer cases, give rise to the phenomenon known as life."—
Practically any astronomy book of the early 20th Century.

The storm was still rising. He had long since ceased to struggle
against it, although the ascending gas streams were carrying him
into the bitterly cold regions ten thousand miles above his normal
level. Dimly he was aware of his mistake: he should never have
entered the area of disturbance, but the spot had developed so
swiftly that there was now no chance of escape. The million-miles-
an-hour wind had seized him as it rose from the depths and was
carrying him up the great funnel it had torn in the photosphere—a
tunnel already large enough to engulf a hundred worlds.
It was very cold. Around him carbon vapour was condensing in

64

clouds of incandescent dust, swiftly torn away by the raging winds. This was something he had never met before, but the short-lived particles of solid matter left no sensation as they whipped through his body. Presently they were no more than glowing streamers far below, their furious movement foreshortened to a gentle undulation.

He was now at a truly enormous height, and his velocity showed no signs of slackening. The horizon was almost fifty thousand miles away, and the whole of the great spot lay visible beneath. Although he possessed neither eyes nor organs of sight, the radiation patterns sweeping through his body built up a picture of the awesome scene below. Like a great wound through which the Sun's life was ebbing into space, the vortex was now thousands of miles deep. From one edge a long tongue of flame was reaching out to form a half-completed bridge, defying the gales sweeping vertically past it. In a few hours, if it survived, it might span the abyss and divide the spot in twain. The fragments would drift apart, the fires of the photosphere would overwhelm them, and soon the great globe would be unblemished again.

The Sun was still receding, and gradually into his slow, dim consciousness came the understanding that he could never return. The eruption that had hurled him into space had not given him sufficient velocity to escape forever, but a second giant force was beginning to exert its power. All his life he had been subjected to the fierce bombardment of solar radiation, pouring upon him from all directions. It was doing so no longer. The Sun now lay far beneath, and the force of its radiation was driving him out into space like a mighty wind. The great cloud of ions that was his body, more tenuous than air, was falling swiftly into the outer darkness.

Now the Sun was a globe of fire shrinking far behind, and the great spot no more than a black stain near the centre of its disc. Ahead lay darkness, utterly unrelieved, for his senses were far too coarse ever to detect the feeble light of the stars or the pale gleam of the circling planets. The only source of light he could ever know was dwindling from him. In a desperate effort to conserve his energy, he drew his body together into a tight, spherical cloud. Now he was almost as dense as air, but the electrostatic repulsion between his billions of constituent ions was too great for further concentration. When at last his strength weakened, they would disperse into space and no trace of his existence would remain.

He never felt the increasing gravitational pull from far ahead, and was unconscious of his changing speed. But presently the first faint intimations of the approaching magnetic field reached his consciousness and stirred it into sluggish life. He strained his senses out into the darkness, but to a creature whose home was the photosphere of the Sun the light of all other bodies was billions of times too faint even to be glimpsed, and the steadily strengthening field through which he was falling was an enigma beyond the comprehension of his rudimentary mind.

The tenuous outer fringes of the atmosphere checked his speed, and he fell slowly towards the invisible planet. Twice he felt a strange, tearing wrench as he passed through the ionosphere; then, no faster than a falling snowflake, he was drifting down through the cold, dense gas of the lower air. The descent took many hours and his strength was waning when he came to rest on a surface hard beyond anything he had ever imagined.

The waters of the Atlantic were bathed with brilliant sunlight, but to him the darkness was absolute save for the faint gleam of the infinitely distant Sun. For aeons he lay, incapable of movement, while the fires of consciousness burned lower within him and the last remnants of his energy ebbed away into the inconceivable cold.

It was long before he noticed the strange new radiation pulsing far off in the darkness—radiation of a kind he had never experienced before. Sluggishly he turned his mind towards it, considering what it might be and whence it came. It was closer than he had thought, for its movement was clearly visible and now it was climbing into the sky, approaching the Sun itself. But this was no second sun, for the strange illumination was waxing and waning, and only for a fraction of a cycle was it shining full upon him.

Nearer and nearer came that enigmatic glare; and as the throbbing rhythm of its brilliance grew fiercer he became aware of a strange, tearing resonance that seemed to shake the whole of his being. Now it was beating down upon him like a flail, tearing into his vitals and loosening his last hold on life itself. He had lost all control over the outer regions of his compressed but still enormous body.

The end came swiftly. The intolerable radiance was directly overhead, no longer pulsing but pouring down upon him in one continuous flood. Then there was neither pain nor wonder, nor the dull longing for the great golden world he had lost for ever . . .

From the streamlined fairing beneath the great flying-wing, the long pencil of the radar beam was sweeping the Atlantic to the horizon's edge. Spinning in synchronism on the Plan Position Indicator, the faintly visible line of the time-base built up a picture of all that lay beneath. At the moment the screen was empty, for the coast of Ireland was more than three hundred miles away. Apart from an occasional brilliant blue spot—which was all that the greatest surface vessel became from fifty thousand feet—nothing would be visible until, in three hours' time, the eastern seaboard of America began to drift into the picture.

The navigator, checking his position continually by the North Atlantic radio lattice, seldom had any need for this part of the

66

liner's radar. But to the passengers, the big skiatron indicator on the promenade deck was a source of constant interest, especially when the weather was bad and there was nothing to be seen below but the undulating hills and valleys of the cloud ceiling. There was still something magical, even in this age, about a radar landfall. No matter how often one had seen it before, it was fascinating to watch the pattern of the coastline forming on the screen, to pick out the harbours and the shipping and, presently, the hills and rivers and lakes of the land beneath.

To Edward Lindsey, returning from a week's leave in Europe, the Plan Position Indicator had a double interest. Fifteen years ago, as a young Coastal Command radio observer in the War of Liberation, he had spent long and tiring hours over these same waters, peering into a primitive forerunner of the great five-foot screen before him. He smiled wryly as his mind went back to those days. What would he have thought then, he wondered, if he could have seen himself as he was now, a prosperous accountant, travelling in comfort ten miles above the Atlantic at almost the velocity of sound? He thought also of the rest of S for Sugar's crew, and wondered what had happened to them in the intervening years.

At the edge of the scan, just crossing the three-hundred-mile range circle, a faint patch of light was beginning to drift into the picture. That was strange: there was no land there, for the Azores were further to the south. Besides, this seemed too ill-defined too be an island. The only thing it could possibly was a storm-cloud heavy with rain.

Lindsey walked to the nearest window and looked out. The weather was extraordinarily fine. Far below, the waters of the Atlantic were crawling eastward towards Europe; even down to the horizon the sky was blue and cloudless.

He went back to the P.P.I. The echo was certainly a very curious one, approximately oval and as far as he could judge about ten miles long, although it was still too far away for accurate measurement. Lindsey did some rapid mental arithmetic. In twenty-five minutes it should be almost underneath them, for it was neatly bisected by the bright line that represented the aircraft's heading. Track? Course? Lord, how quickly one forgot that sort of thing! But it didn't matter—the wind could make little difference at the speed they were travelling. He would come back and have a look at it then, unless the gang in the bar got hold of him again.

Twenty minutes later he was even more puzzled. The tiny blue oval of light gleaming on the dark face of the screen was now only fifty miles away. If it were indeed a cloud, it was the strangest one he had ever seen. But the scale of the picture was still too small for him to make out any details.

The main controls of the indicator were safely locked away

beneath the notice which read: PASSENGERS ARE REQUESTED NOT TO PLACE EMPTY GLASSES ON THE SKIATRON. However, one control had been left for the use of all comers. A massive three-position switch—guaranteed unbreakable—enabled anyone to select the tube's three different ranges: three hundred, fifty, and ten miles. Normally the three-hundred-mile picture was used, but the more restricted fifty-mile scan gave much greater detail and was excellent for sightseeing overland. The ten-mile range was quite useless and no one knew why it was there.

Lindsey turned the switch to 50, and the picture seemed to explode. The mysterious echo, which had been nearing the screen's centre, now lay at its edge once more, enlarged six-fold. Lindsey waited until the afterglow of the old picture had died away; then he leaned over and carefully examined the new.

The echo almost filled the gap between the forty- and fifty-mile range circles, and now that he could see it clearly its strangeness almost took his breath away. From its centre radiated a curious network of filaments, while at its heart glowed a bright area perhaps two miles in length. It could only be fancy—yet he could have sworn that the central spot was pulsing very slowly.

Almost unable to believe his eyes, Lindsey stared into the screen. He watched in hypnotized fascination until the oval mist was less than forty miles away; then he ran to the nearest telephone and called for one of the ship's radio officers. While he was waiting, he went again to the observation port and looked out at the ocean beneath. He could see for at least a hundred miles—but there was absolutely nothing there but the blue Atlantic and the open sky.

It was a long walk from the control room to the promenade deck, and when Sub-Lieutenant Armstrong arrived, concealing his annoyance beneath a mask of polite but not obsequious service, the object was less than twenty miles away. Lindsey pointed to the skiatron.

"Look!" he said simply.

Sub-Lieutenant Armstrong looked. For a moment there was silence. Then came a curious, half-strangled ejaculation and he jumped back as if he had been stung. He leaned forward again and rubbed at the screen with his sleeve as if trying to remove something that shouldn't be there. Stopping himself in time, he grinned foolishly at Lindsey. Then he went to the observation window.

"There's nothing there. I've looked," said Lindsey.

After the initial shock, Armstrong moved with commendable speed. He ran back to the skiatron, unlocked the controls with his master key, and made a series of swift adjustments. At once the time-base began to whirl round at a greatly increased speed, giving a more continuous picture than before.

It was much clearer now. The bright nucleus *was* pulsating, and faint knots of light were moving slowly outward along the radiating filaments. As he stared, fascinated, Lindsey suddenly remembered a glimpse he had once of an amoeba under the microscope. Apparently the same thought had occurred to the Sub-Lieutenant.

"It—it looks alive!" he whispered incredulously.

"I know," said Lindsey. "What do you think it is?"

The other hesitated for a while. "I remember reading once that Appleton or someone had detected patches of ionization low down in the atmosphere. That's the only thing it can be."

"But its structure! How do you explain that?"

The other shrugged his shoulders. "I can't," he said bluntly.

It was vertically beneath them now, disappearing into the blind area at the centre of the screen. While they were waiting for it to emerge again they had another look at the ocean below. It was uncanny: there was still absolutely nothing to be seen. But the radar could not lie. Something *must* be there—

It was fading fast when it reappeared a minute later, fading as if the full power of the radar transmitter had destroyed its cohesion. For the filaments were breaking up, and even as they watched the ten-mile-long oval began to disintegrate. There was something awe-inspiring about the sight, and for some unfathomable reason Lindsey felt a surge of pity, as though he were witnessing the death of some gigantic beast. He shook his head angrily, but he could not get the thought out of his mind.

Twenty miles away, the last traces of ionization were dispersing to the winds. Soon eye and radar screen alike saw only the unbroken waters of the Atlantic rolling endlessly eastwards as if no power could ever disturb them.

And across the screen of the great indicator, two men stared speechlessly at one another, each afraid to guess what lay in the other's mind.

THE HOUR OF BATTLE

BY ROBERT SHECKLEY

Of all the bright new talents to emerge in S.F. in recent years, few show a wider promise than the youthful American, *Robert Sheckley*. In the space of a few years his short stories and novels —in particular the revolutionary "The Status Civilisation"— have created a lasting impression on readers throughout the world. Sheckley contributes extensively to the various top publications in the genre and frequently mingles some strong shades of horror with his work—this is probably seen to best advantage in "Untouched By Human Hands". In the story reprinted here the tension of galactic warfare is steadily built to a magnificient climax. More, Mr. Sheckley, more!

"That hand didn't move, did it?" Edwardson asked, standing at the port, looking at the stars.

"No," Morse said. He had been staring fixedly at the Attison Detector for over an hour. Now he blinked three times rapidly, and looked again. "Not a millimetre."

"I don't think it moved either," Cassel added, from behind the gunfire panel. And that was that. The slender black hand of the indicator rested unwaveringly on zero. The ship's guns were ready, their black mouths open to the stars. A steady hum filled the room. It came from the Attison Detector and the sound was reassuring. It reinforced the fact that the Detector was attached to all the other Detectors, forming a gigantic network around Earth.

"Why in hell don't they come?" Edwardson asked, still looking at the stars. "Why don't they hit?"

"Aah, shut up," Morse said. He had a tired, glum look. High on his right temple was an old radiation burn, a sunburst of pink scar tissue. From a distance it looked like a decoration.

"I just wish they'd come," Edwardson said. He returned from the port of his chair, bending to clear the low metal ceiling. "Don't you wish they'd come?" Edwardson had the narrow, timid face of a mouse; but a highly intelligent mouse. One that cats did well to avoid.

"Don't you?" he repeated.

The other men didn't answer. They had settled back to their dreams, staring hypnotically at the Detector face.

70

"They've had enough time," Edwardson said, half to himself.

Cassel yawned and licked his lips. "Anyone want to play some gin?" he asked, stroking his beard, The beard was a memento of his undergraduate days. Cassel maintained he could store almost fifteen minutes worth of oxygen in its follicles. He had never stepped into space unhelmeted to prove it.

Morse looked away, and Edwardson automatically watched the indicator. This routine had been drilled into them, branded into their subconscious. They would as soon have cut their throats as leave the indicator unguarded.

"Do you think they'll come soon?" Edwardson asked, his brown rodent's eyes on the indicator. The men didn't answer him. After two months together in space their conversational powers were exhausted. They weren't interested in Cassel's undergraduate days, or in Morse's conquests.

They were bored to death even with their own thoughts and dreams, bored with the attack they expected momentarily.

"Just one thing *I'd* like to know," Edwardson said, slipping with ease into an old conversational gambit. "How far can they do it?"

They had talked for weeks about the enemy's telepathic range, but they always returned to it.

As professional soldiers, they couldn't help but speculate on the enemy and his weapons. It was their shop talk.

"Well," Morse said wearily, "Our Detector network covers the system out beyond Mars' orbit."

"Where we sit," Cassel said, watching the indicators now that the others were talking.

"They might not even know we have a detection unit working," Morse said, as he had said a thousand times.

"Oh, stop," Edwardson said, his thin face twisted in scorn. "They're telepathic. They must have read every bit of stuff in Everset's mind."

"Everset didn't know we had a detection unit," Morse said, his eyes returning to the dial. "He was captured before we had it."

"Look," Edwardson said, "They ask him, 'Boy, what would you do if you knew a telepathic race was coming to take over Earth? How would you guard the planet?'"

"Idle speculation," Cassel said. "Maybe Everset didn't think of this."

"He thinks like a man, doesn't he? Everyone agreed on this defence. Everset would, too."

"Sillogistic," Cassel murmured. "Very shaky."

"I sure wish he hadn't been captured," Edwardson said.

"It could have been worse," Morse put in, his face sadder than ever. "What if they'd captured *both* of them?"

"I wish they'd come," Edwardson said.

Richard Everset and C. R. Jones had gone on the first intersteller flight. They had found an inhabited planet in the region of Vega. The rest was standard procedure.

A flip of the coin had decided it. Everset went down in the scouter, maintaining radio contact with Jones, in the ship.

The recording of that contact was preserved for all Earth to hear.

"Just met the natives," Everset said. "Funny looking bunch. Give you the physical description later."

"Are they trying to talk to you?" Jones asked, guiding the ship in a slow spiral over the planet.

"No. Hold it. Well I'm damned! They're telepathic! How do you like that?"

"Great," Jones said. "Go on."

"Hold it. Say, Jonesy, I don't know as I like these boys. They haven't got nice minds. Brother!"

"What is it?" Jones asked, lifting the ship a little higher.

"Minds! These bastards are power-crazy. Seems they've hit all the systems around here, looking for someone to—"

"Yeh?"

"I've got that a bit wrong," Everset said pleasantly. "They are not so bad."

Jones had a quick mind, a suspicious nature and good reflexes. He set the accelerator for all the G's he could take, lay down on the floor and said. "Tell me more."

"Come on down," Everset said, in violation of every law of space-flight. "These guys are all right. As a matter of fact, they're the most marvellous—"

That was where the recording ended, because Jones was pinned to the floor by twenty G's acceleration as he boosted the ship to the level needed for the C-jump.

He broke three ribs getting home, but he got there.

A telepathic species was on the march. What was Earth going to do about it?

A lot of speculation necessarily clothed the bare bones of Jones' information. Evidently the species could take over a mind with ease. With Everset, it seemed that they had insinuated their thoughts into his, delicately altering his previous convictions. They had possessed him with remarkable ease.

How about Jones? Why hadn't they taken him? Was distance a factor? Or hadn't they been prepared for the suddenness of his departure?

One thing was certain. Everything Everset knew, the enemy knew. That meant they knew where Earth was, and how defenceless the planet was to their form of attack.

It could be expected that they were on their way.

Something was needed to nullify their tremendous advantage. But what sort of something? What armour is there against thought? How do you dodge a wavelength?

Pouched-eyed scientists gravely consulted their periodic tables.

And how do you know when a man has been possessed? Although the enemy was clumsy with Everset, would they continue to be clumsy? Wouldn't they learn?

Psychologists tore their hair and bewailed the absence of an absolute scale for humanity.

Of course, something had to be done at once. The answer, from a technological planet, was a technological one. Build a space fleet and equip it with some sort of a detection-fire network.

This was done in record time. The Attison Detector was developed, a cross between radar and the electroencephalograph. Any alteration from the typical-human brain wave pattern of the occupants of a Detector-equipped ship would boost the indicator around the dial. Even a bad dream or a case of indigestion would jar it.

It seemed probable that any attempt to take over a human mind would disturb something. There had to be a point of interaction, somewhere.

That was what the Attison Detector was supposed to detect. Maybe it would.

The spaceships, three men to a ship, dotted space between Earth and Mars, forming a gigantic sphere with Earth in the centre.

Tens of thousands of men crouched behind gunfire panels, watching the dials on the Attison Detector.

The unmoving dials.

"Do you think I could fire a couple of bursts?" Edwardson asked, his fingers on the gunfire button. "Just to limber the guns?"

"Those guns don't need limbering," Cassel said, stroking his beard. "Besides, you'd throw the whole fleet into a panic."

"Cassel," Morse said, very quietly. "Get your hands off that beard."

"Why should I?" Cassel asked.

"Because," Morse answered, almost in a whisper, "I am about to ram it right down your fat throat."

Cassel grinned and tightened his fists. "Pleasure," he said. "I'm tired of looking at that scar of yours." He stood up.

"Cut it," Edwardson said wearily. "Watch the birdie."

"No reason to, really," Morse said, leaning back. "There's an alarm bell attached." But he looked at the dial.

"What if the bell doesn't work?" Edwardson asked. "What if the dial is jammed? How would you like something cold slithering into your mind?"

"The dial'll work," Cassel said. His eyes shifted from Edwardson's face to the motionless indicator.

"I think I'll sack in," Edwardson said.

"Stick around," Cassel said. "Play you some gin."

"All right," Edwardson found and shuffled the greasy cards, while Morse took a turn glaring at the dial.

"I sure wish they'd come," he said.

"Cut," Edwardson said, handing the pack to Cassel.

"I wonder what our friends look like," Morse said, watching the dial.

"Probably remarkably like us," Edwardson said, dealing the cards. Cassel picked them up one by one, slowly, as if he hoped something interesting would be under them.

"They should have given us another man," Cassel said. "We could play bridge."

"I don't play bridge," Edwardson said.

"You could learn."

"Why didn't we send a task force?" Morse asked. "Why didn't we bomb their planet?"

"Don't be dumb," Edwardson said. "We'd lose any ship we sent. Probably get them back at us, possessed and firing."

"Knock with nine," Cassel said.

"I don't give a good damn if you knock with a thousand," Edwardson said gaily. "How much do I owe you now?"

"Three million five hundred and eight thousand and ten Dollars."

"I sure wish they'd come," Morse said.

"Want me to write a cheque?"

"Take your time. Take until next week."

"Someone should reason with the bastards," Morse said, looking out the port. Cassel immediately looked at the dial.

"I just thought of something," Edwardson said.

"Yeh?"

"I bet it feels horrible to have your mind grabbed," Edwardson said. "I bet it's awful."

"You'll know when it happens," Cassell said.

"Did Everset?"

"Probably. He just couldn't do anything about it."

"My mind feels fine," Cassel said. "But the first one of you guys starts acting queer—watch out."

They all laughed.

"Well," Edwardson said, "I'd sure like a chance to reason with them. This is stupid."

"Why not?" Cassel asked.

"You mean go out and meet *them*?"

"Sure," Cassel said. "We're doing no good sitting here."

"I should think we could do something," Edwardson said slowly. "After all, they're not invincible. They're reasoning beings."

Morse punched a course on the ship's tape, then looked up.

"You think we should contact the command? Tell them what we're doing?"

"No!" Cassel said and Edwardson nodded in agreement. "Red tape. We'll just go out and see what we can do. If they won't talk, we'll blast 'em out of space."

"Look!"

Out of the port they could see the red flare of a reaction engine; the next ship in their sector, speeding forward.

"They must have got the same idea," Edwardson said.

"Let's get there first," Cassel said. Morse shoved the accelerator in and they were thrown back in their seats.

"That dial hasn't moved yet, has it?" Edwardson asked, over the clamour of the Detector alarm bell.

"Not a move out of it," Cassel said, looking at the dial with its indicator slammed all the way over to the highest notch.

EQUATOR

BY BRIAN ALDISS

> *Brian Aldiss* is Britain's major contribution to the ranks of the
> top modern Science Fiction writers. With a series of well-
> plotted, imaginative and totally engrossing works he has won a
> wide following on both sides of the Atlantic—apart from carry-
> ing off a number of top literary prizes. A newspaperman by
> profession, Aldiss displays a questing mind in his writing and a
> rather special ability to combine flights of fancy with concrete
> facts. This novelette of insurgence and espionage set against a
> background of Sumatra—which Aldiss knows—is an inter-
> esting experiment in S.F.; and dating as it does from 1958,
> marks quite a definite turning point in the author's career.
> Settle yourself well, this is not an easy story to put down.

I

Evening shadows came across the spaceport in long strides. It
was the one time of day when you could almost feel the world
rotating. In the rays of the sinking sun, dusty palms round the
spaceport looked like so many varnished cardboard props. By
day, these palms seemed metal; by evening, so much *papier maché*
In the tropics, nothing was itself, merely fabric stretched over heat,
poses over pulses.

The palms bowed stiffly as Scout Ship AX25 blasted up into the
sky, peppering them with another spray of dust.

The three occupants of the ship were rocked back on their
acceleration couches for only a few seconds. Then Allan Cunliffe
got up, strolled casually over to the port and gazed out. Nobody
would guess from his composed face that the ship had just em-
barked on a hazardous mission.

"At once you begin to live," he said, looking down at the world
with a kind of pride.

His friend, Tyne Leslie, nodded in an attempt at agreement.
It was the best, at the moment, that he could do. Joining Allan,
he too looked out.

Already, he observed wonderingly, the mighty panorama of
sunset was only a red stain on a carpet below them; Sumatra lay
across the equator like a roasting fish on a spit. Outside: a starry
void. In his stomach: another starry void.

At once you begin to live . . . But this was Tyne's first trip on the spy patrol; living meant extra adrenalin walloping through his heart valves, the centipede track of prickles over his skin, the starry void in the lesser intestine.

"It's the sort of feeling you don't get behind an office desk," he said. Chalk one up to the office desk, he thought.

Allan nodded, saying nothing. His silences were always positive. When the rest of the world was talking as it never had before, Allan Cunliffe remained silent. Certainly he had as many mixed feelings about the Rosks as anyone else on Earth: but he kept the lid on them. It was that quality as much as any other that had guaranteed a firm friendship between Allan and Tyne, long before the latter followed his friend's lead and joined the Space Service.

"Let's get forward and see Murray," Allan said, clapping Tyne on the back. Undoubtedly he had divined something of the other's feelings.

The scout was small, one of the Bristol-Cunard "Hynam" line, a three-berth job with light armament and Betson-Watson "Medmenham X" accelerators. The third member of the team, its leader, was Captain Murray Mumford, one of the first men ever to set eyes on the Rosks, four years ago.

He grinned at the other two as they came into the cabin, set the autopilot, and turned round to face them.

"Lunar in five and a fraction hours," he said. Once you had seen Murray, you would never forget him. Physically he was no more and no less than a superb specimen of broad-shouldered manhood. Five minutes with him convinced you that he had that extraordinary persuasive ability which, without a word being said, could convert potential rivals into admirers. Tyne, always sensitive to the currents of human feelings, was aware of this magnetic quality of Murray's; he distrusted it merely because he knew Murray himself was aware of it and frequently used it to his own advantage.

"Well, what's the picture?" he asked, accepting a mescahale from Allan, trying to appear at ease.

"With any luck, we'll have a pretty quiet job for your first live op," Murray replied, as they lit their mescahales. "The target area, as you know, is Luna Area 101. Luna Intelligence reports a new object outside one of the Roskian domes. It's small and immobile —so far, at any rate. It's outside a dome on the southern perimeter of Area 101, which means it is fairly accessible from our point of view."

"What's the state of light there now, Murray?" Allan asked.

"Sundown in Grimaldi, which contains Area 101, was four hours ago. Intelligence suspects the Rosks may be planning something under cover of darkness; we have imposed a lot of shipping

77

restrictions on their Earth-Luna route lately. So our orders are to slip in from the night side and investigate—obviously without being seen, if possible. Just a quick look over, personal inspection in spacesuits. We should not be out of the ship for more than twenty minutes. Then we streak for home again, heroes all."

The starry void blossomed up again in Tyne's midriff. Action; this was what he feared and what he wanted. He looked at the lunar map Murray carelessly indicated. One small square of it, low in the third quadrant covering Grimaldi, had been shaded yellow. This was Area 101. Beside it, in the same yellow crayon, one word had been written: Rosk.

Tyne noticed Murray studying his face intently, and turned away. "World Government made a great mistake in allowing the Rosks a base away from Earth," he said.

"You were the diplomat when Allan and I were just squaddies in the Space Service," Murray said, smiling. "You tell us why Area 101 was conceded to them."

"The official reason given," Allan said, stepping in to back up his friend, "was that while we were being kind to aliens we could not expect a space-travelling race to be pinned to one planet; we were morally obliged to cede a part of Grimaldi, so that they could indulge in Earth-Moon flight."

"Yes, that was the official face-saver." Tyne agreed. "Whenever it is beaten on any point of an agenda, World Government, the United Nations Council, declares itself 'morally obliged'. In actual fact, we had rings made round us. The Rosks are so much better at argument and debate than we are, that at first they could talk themselves into anything they wanted."

"And now the Space Service sorts out the results of the politicians' muddle," Murray said. It sounded slightly like a personal jibe; Tyne could not forget he had once been in politics; and in his present state of tension, he did not ignore the remark.

"You'd better ask yourself how fine a job the S.S. is doing, Murray. Human-Roskian relations have deteriorated to such an extent this last year, that if we get caught in Area 101, we may well precipitate a war."

"Spoken like a diplomat!" Murray exclaimed sarcastically.

The three of them spent most of the next four and a half hours reading, hardly speaking at all.

"Better look alert. Put your books away," Murray said suddenly, jumping up and returning to the cabin.

"Don't mind Murray; he often behaves like a musclebound schoolmaster," Allan said laughing.

Not often, Tyne admitted to himself without bothering to contradict his friend aloud. Murray had drunk with them several times at the Madeka Hotel in Sumatra; his manner then had been

78

far from schoolmasterly. He thought of Murray knocking back carioka till the early hours, rising later to eat with a monstrous appetite, while Allan and Tyne beside him pushed away at the large unappetizing breakfast the hotel provided.

The immediate present eclipsed Tyne's thoughts as the great black segment of moon slid up at them. It was like falling into a smile-shaped hole. Radar-guided, the scout became a tiny, moving chip of a ship again, instead of a little world in its own right.

A few lights gleamed far ahead: Rosk lights, shining up from Area 101.

"Strap in!" Murray said, over the intercom.

They were braking. As deceleration increased, it felt as if they were plunging through water, then soup, then treacle, then wood. Then they weren't plunging at all. They were feather-light. With a bump, they stopped. They were down.

"All change; please have your alien identity cards ready!" said Allan. Tyne wondered how he was feeling, even as Allan smiled reassuringly at him.

Murray left the cabin, walking with something like a swagger. He was pleasantly excited. For him, this was the simple life, with no cares but the present one.

"The radar-baffle's on," he said. "No signs of alarm from our friends outside. Let's get into our suits as fast as possible."

They climbed into the spacesuits. The process took half an hour, during which Tyne sweated freely, wondering all the while if their ship had been sighted by Rosk lookouts. But there was no alternative. The spacesuit is a tool: a bulky, complex, hazardous, pernickety tool for surviving where one is not meant to survive. It needs endless adjustment before it can be trusted. There was not a spacer in the system who did not hate spacesuits, or envy the Rosks their immeasurably superior variety.

At last they had lashed, strapped, dogged and screwed each other into place. Three monstrous robots bumbled round slowly in the confined space, nearly filling the ship with their bulk; they made with slow, underwater, gestures for the hatch. Five minutes later, they were all standing on the lunar surface in complete darkness.

In what were already regarded as the old palmy days, before the Rosks arrived in the system, Tyne had frequently been up to the moon, on pleasure and business. He was not prepared for how bleakly uninviting the place appeared now. In the Grade-A darkness, Grimaldi was a desert of frozen soot.

"We've something less than half a mile to the target dome," Murray said, his voice a whisper in the headsets. "Let's move!"

They saw by infra-red extensions. Murray led them along by the crater edge, treading round spines of outcropping debris. The alien domes became visible as black breasts against sequin-studded silk. Through the little grille of his suit window. Tyne saw the world as a plaster mock-up of a reality too unreal ever to be true. He himself was a pigmy imprisoned in the iron bowel of a robot heading for destruction. Fighting off that irrational sensation, he peered ahead for the strange object they had come to investigate.

Something lay ahead. It was impossible to see what it was. Tyne touched Allan's arm. The latter swung round, and then stared in the direction in which Tyne pointed. Murray paused, making a clumsily impatient gesture to them to come on. Perhaps he feels vulnerable as I do, Tyne thought, sympathetically, pointing again through the blackness for Murray's benefit.

Next second, they were bathed in the ashy glare of a searchlight, skewered neatly in mid-gesutre.

The light came not from the domes ahead, but to one side, from a point by the crater wall. Tyne just stood there, blinded, knowing they were trapped.

"Drop!" Allan shouted.

"Shoot the light out!" Murray said. His great metal-claw went down piston-fashion to the service pistol, came up levelling the cumbrous weapon, jerked with the recoil. Allan and Tyne heard the shots only as vibrant thuds through Murray's suit mike.

He got the light. It cut off—but already another beam was striking out from the nearest dome, swerving and sending an oval across the ash towards them. Probably they were being fired at, Tyne thought detachedly; you would not know until you were hit. He had his pistol out and was firing too, rather wildly, but towards where the enemy attack would come from.

"Here they come! Make for the ship, Tyne!" Allan bellowed. As the new searchlight swamped them, Tyne caught a glimpse of moving forms. The Rosks had been lying in wait for them. Then a hammerblow struck his shoulder, sending illuminated pain like a crazy neon system all over his body. Gasping, he heard his suit creak with all the abandon of a falling tree. He was going over . . . and as he went, he had a jigsaw puzzle, upside-down, glimpse of approaching Rosks.

When the Rosks had arrived in the solar system four and a half years before, one unambitious day in March, 2189, an epoch ended, though comparatively few people realized it at the time. Man's time of isolation was over. No longer could he regard himself as the only sentient being in the universe. On his doorstep stood a race superior to him scientifically if not morally.

The shock of the Roskian arrival was felt most severely in those countries which for several centuries had been accustomed to regarding themselves as the world's rulers, or the arbiters of its conduct. They were now in the position of a school bully, who, looking carefully over his shoulder, finds the headmaster standing over him.

The Rosks came in one mighty ship, and a quarter of the world's population quaked in fear; another quarter cheered with excitement; the wiser half reserved judgment. Some of them, four and a half years later, were still reserving judgment. The Rosks were no easier to sum up than Earthmen.

Superficially, a Rosk resembled a man. Not a white man but, say, a Malayan. Their appearance varied from one to another, but most of them had light brown skins, no bridge to their noses, dark eyes. Their body temperature was 105.1 degrees, a sign of the hotter planet from which they came.

When the Rosks arrived, Tyne Leslie was the youngest second secretary to an under-secretary to the Under-Secretary of the British Corps of the United Nations Council. He had witnessed the endless fluttering in ministerial dovecotes that went on all over the world as the realities of the Rosk-Man situation became apparent. For the true situation emerged only gradually, while language barriers were being broken down. And the true situation was both complicated and unpleasant.

Man learnt something of this impasse from a yellow-haired Rosk, Tawdell Co Barr, who was one of the first Roskian spokesmen on the U.N.C.

"Our mother ship," he explained, "is an interstellar vessel housing four interplanetary craft and something more than five thousand of our people, male and female. Most of them are colonists, seeking only a world to live in, We have come from a world you would call Alpha Centauri II; ours is the first interstellar voyage ever made from that beautiful but overcrowded planet. We came to Sol, our nearest neighbour in the vastness of space, seeking room to live—only to find that its one habitable planet is already swarming with men. Although we are happy to meet another sentient race, the depth of our disappointment otherwise cannot be measured: our journey, our long journey, has been in vain."

"It's a civil speech," Tyne commented, when he heard it. And other civil speeches followed, each revealing at least one awkward fact about the Rosk visit.

To begin with, these facts almost passed unnoticed among the general run of humanity.

After the first wave of shock had passed round Earth, a tide of optimism followed. The real difficulties inherent in the situation only emerged later. Rosks were heroes; most people managed successfully to hide their disappointment at the lack of bug eyes and tentacles in the visitors. Nor did they worry when Tawdell Co Barr revealed that the Roskian political system was a dictatorship under the supreme Ap II Dowl.

Civility, in fact—an uneasy civility on Earth's part—was the order of the day. The big ship circled Earth inside the lunar orbit, a handful of Rosks came down and fraternized, speaking either to the councillors of the U.N.C. or over tridee to the multitude; or they visited some of the cities of Earth.

In return for this hospitality, they presented men with microfilm books about natural and social life on Alpha Centauri II, as well as specimens of their literature and art, and preserved samples of their flora. But no Earthman was allowed to enter their ship. Scientists, politicians, celebrities, newsmen, all were politely refused admittance, and provided with acceptable explanations.

"Our ship is as inviting as a charnel house," Co Barr admitted, gravely. "Many of our people died on the journey here. Many are dying now, from dietary or sunlight deficiencies, or from mental illnesses brought about by lifelong incarceration. For we have been exiled for two exhausting generations in the night of space. We can go no further. All we ask, all we beg of you, in your mercy, is a place in which we may rest and recover from our ordeal."

A place . . . But what place? At first it seemed an almost impossible question; the U.N.C. convened practically without a break for weeks on end. For the first time in centuries, all nations were united—in a determination not to allow the Rosks onto their territory.

In the end, two decisions emerged. First, that the Rosks should be granted an Earth base. Second, where it should be.

Both answers were inevitable. Even Tyne, from his back seat in the debate, saw them coming. In the human attitude to the Rosks lay both fear and envy; even if mercy should permit it, it was impossible to demand of the Rosks that they leave the solar system again. Such a move might provoke them to defiance of man. They might in desperation fight for the land they required. And what weapons they might possess was unknown; indeed, what gifts their science might yield upon more intimate aquaintance was a matter for general speculation.

As for the site of the base, it had to be in an equatorial region. Earth's equatorial belt was about as warm as Alpha II's temperate zone. A site in the middle of Africa might be too inconvenient; a small island might prove too self-contained. The increasingly mighty nation of Brazil would tolerate no Rosks near her borders. After many squawkings, orations, protests and uses of veto an area of eighty square miles just south of Padang in Sumatra was finally ceded as a Rosk base.

"For this small gift our gratitude is immeasurable," Ap II Dowl, making one of his rare personal visits, said. There were many who considered his choice of adjective unfortunate—or deliberate.

So the Rosks landed on Earth in their massive ship. It soon became clear that they never intended to leave again; they had had enough of space.

Earth was unwilling to play permanent host. The Rosks, multiplying behind a perimeter they had rapidly fortified, represented a threat no less ominous for being unformulated. Yet how to evict them? It seemed to Earth's statesmen that the only possible line of action was to *nag* the Rosks into leaving.

Unfortunately, the more they scratched the sore, the more it itched.

Nation after nation sent its representatives into Sumatra, to see what could be seen, and to pick up any Roskian secrets, if possible. In the big U.N.C. council chambers in Padang, Man and Rosk haggled and talked, demanded and conceded, bluffed and argued. The situation was at once funny and tragic. That old hope of profiting other than materially by the contact of two races was quite lost to view.

Except on diplomatic errands, Earthmen were not allowed into Rosk base, Rosks were not allowed outside it—yet in practice spies on both sides infringed these laws. Padang became full of spies: nation spying against nation, race against race. The situation became more complex still when, in an attempt to ingratiate themselves, the U.N.C. ceded the small Lunar Area 101 to the visitors, to allow them to test out their four interplanetary ships.

"This move touches my heart," Tawdell Co Barr declared. "We came as strangers; you welcome us as friends. Together, Rosk and man will build a new and lasting civilization."

By this time, such fair words rang hollow.

Whether Tawdell meant it or not, the hopes he expressed were the hopes of many men, everywhere. Unfortunately, this was Tawdell's last public speech! He disappeared into the Rosk base and was not heard of again. It was believed in diplomatic circles that the yellow-haired Rosk had been too friendly towards man for his overlords' liking. Ap II Dowl's dictatorship, which had been formed in the harsh environs of the ship, now took the reins. His henchmen sat at the council tables, and relations between the two sides slowly deteriorated.

The spy patrol in which Murray, Allan and Tyne served was only one instance of that deterioration.

II

Something like a lemon. No, a melon. No, it was stretching; a cucumber. No, it was bending; a banana. No, curling; a slice of melon. No, a melon again. Or was it—it was all distorted—was it a face? It rippled, solidified. It took on a firm jaw and eyes staring fixedly down. It became Murray Mumford's face, seen through a haze of weakness.

"Oh," groaned Tyne. He was in a bunk which still rippled at the edges, staring up at Murray.

"How is it?" Murray asked. "Feeling better?"

"Drink of water," Tyne said.

He gulped it down when it was brought. His head cleared, he remembered the incident at 101, the numbing blow on his spacesuit.

"Where are we, Murray?" he asked.

"One hour out from Lunar, unpursued, heading back home," Murray told him. "I was too quick for the Rosks. I thought you were never coming round. How do you feel?"

"This is the best part of me," Tyne said ironically, raising his gloved left hand. Beneath the glove were substitute steel fingers and palm; his real hand had been amputated after an air crash several years ago.

"I don't think there's much more wrong with you," Murray said, "apart from a few bruises. The Rosks fired on us. A bullet hit your suit glancingly on the shoulder; luckily no joints split, and shock absorbers took most of the blow. How do you do it—magic rabbit's foot?"

"How did I get here? Didn't I black out?"

"You blacked out all right, went down like a felled ox. I part-dragged, part-carried you here," Murray said. "Fortunately, as you went down I managed to shoot out the second Rosk searchlight."

"Thanks, Murray," Tyne said, and only then, with a rush of guilt, remembered his friend. "Where's Allan?"

Murray turned away, drawing his thick brows together as if in pain. "I'm afraid Allan didn't make it," he said quietly.

"How do you mean, didn't make it?"

Swinging back to the bunk, as though he had suddenly found the words he wanted, Murray said, "Look, Tyne, this may be difficult for you to take. Things got out of hand back there. It was a nasty spot—you know that. When you went down, I grabbed you and got you over one shoulder. Allan shouted out to me to run for it and leave you there. It must have been a moment of panic, I suppose. He wanted to leave you for the Rosk. I told him to cover my retreat, and the next thing I knew, he was waving his gun in my face, telling me he'd shoot me if I did not drop you!"

"Allan!" Tyne protested. "Allan said that?"

"Have you ever panicked?" Murray asked. "There are situations where your moorings break loose, and you don't know what you are saying or doing. When I saw Allan's gun in my face, and felt the Rosks coming up behind, I—I lost control of what I was doing, too."

He turned his head again, his big body tense in a way Tyne had never seen it before. The man on the bunk felt his mouth go dry as he asked, "What did you do, Murray?"

84

Space slid by outside, sly, snakey, cold as time at a crisis, ignoring Murray as he said, "I shot Allan. Right in the stomach."

Tyne was bound down on his bunk. He could only wave his steel fist and his flesh fist, impotently.

"There was nothing else to do," Murray said savagely, clutching one of the waving wrists. "Listen to me, Tyne, should I have left you there, out cold? We weren't supposed to be in Area 101— we had no legal right. Would you rather have come to with a group of killer Rosks round you? I did the only thing I could. Allan Cunliffe mutinied; as captain, I dealt with it on the spot. There's no more to it than that."

"But I know Allan," Tyne yelled. "How could he—he wouldn't —he's not the sort—"

"We none of us know each other," Murray shouted back. His face was dark, suffused with a feverish look of excitement. "We don't even know ourselves. In a moment of crisis, something takes over from us—our id, or something. That's what happened to Allan. Now shut up, and think things over till you see I did the only possible thing."

He strode forward into the cabin, slamming the door behind him, leaving Tyne alone.

Tyne lay where he was, churning the whole thing over in his brain. He could believe neither that his friend was dead, nor that he had lost control of himself. Yet he could not do other than believe; after all, a submerged rivalry for promotion had always existed between Allan and Murray; perhaps in those frightening seconds in the dark, it had come to a head.

Once before they landed, Murray returned to the crew room, to look in at Tyne. His manner was still tense.

"How are you feeling now?" he asked.

"I don't want to see you," Tyne said grimly. "I'll see you at the court of inquiry. Till then, keep out of my way."

His face setting into harsh lines, Murray came across to the bunk and put his hands over Tyne's throat.

"Watch what you're saying and who you're saying it to," he said. "I've told you the facts. I don't like them any better than you do. If Allan had not suddenly turned coward, he'd be here with us now,"

Tyne brought his steel left hand over, clasping the other's wrist, squeezing, squeezing. Letting out a gasp of pain, Murray pulled his arm away; a bracelet of red flesh encircled it. He allowed Tyne one look of malice, then went back and shut himself in the cabin. It was the last Tyne would see of him for a surprisingly long while.

When they landed, Tyne lay patiently for a time, then bellowed for Murray to come and release him. Webbed straps, fastening under the bunk, ensured that he could not release himself. No answer came to his shouts. After twenty minutes, the rear air lock opened, and two Sumatran medical orderlies entered with a stretcher.

From them, Tyne gathered that he was back at Patrol H.Q. Murray had phoned straight through to the hospital, telling them to collect him from the scout for examination.

"I'll come round for examination later," Tyne said, testily. "Right now, I have to report to the Commander."

"Don't worry; the Commander has already been informed about the state of your health," one of the orderlies said.

Despite Tyne's protests, the man was adamant. From his replies, it seemed as if Murray had cast some doubts on Tyne's sanity. So Tyne was carted to the militaty hospital on a stretcher.

Procedure there was no more rapid than in any other hospital. It took the doctors a long while to decide that Tyne Leslie was sane but savage, bruised but sound. In between the examinations were periods of waiting. All this, Tyne thought angrily, smoking his way through a packet of mescahales, was Murray's doing: the scout captain had fixed this so that Tyne's report was delayed. Well, he would fix Murray. Murray was going to be in trouble.

After two hours, buttoning up his uniform, he hurried over to Squadron Office. There a surprise awaited him. Murray had not reported in from his mission. Murray had not been seen. Suspicion and curiosity brewing in his mind, Tyne hurried over to the billets where the squadron lived. Nobody there had seen Murray either; his room was empty, none of his kit disturbed. Over his bed, a pretty half-caste girl stared saucily, blankly, from her photograph. Written in babyish letters across it were the words "Love from Mina."

The sun was gathering its full, mid-morning glory about it. Ignoring it, Tyne ran to the main gate to question the traffic cop on duty under his concrete umbrella. Yes, Captain Mumford had left in a staff car just after breakfast, heading for town.

"Thanks," Tyne said. He thumbed a lift into town himself, riding the five miles of dust and sunshine in grim impatience.

He knew he should have reported in properly before leaving camp; above all he should have reported Allan's death. But in an obscure way he felt time to be vital. Murray had inexplicably disappeared; it would be easier to find him while the trail was hot. The time was 10.50.

Padang was one of the most interesting cities on Earth. To every layer of its life, the nearness of the Rosk base gave an agreeable frisson of excitement. The feeling that something gigantic might happen any day hovered over its hot, scented streets. It was an international city. Among the native Indonesians and Chinese moved U.N.C. delegates from all over the Earth, or their wives, mistresses or followers. Street vendors hawked national emblems of every conceivable kind, from rising suns to leeks. It was also an inter-system city, the first on Earth, for Roskian U.N.C. delegates, prominently displaying their lapel permits, strolled through the city or sat at restaurants. It was, above all, a boom city. Along the gay Tida App, skyscrapers rose. Among the palms, the shanties, the picturesque two-storey streets: solid blocks of flats rising. Above the crows: fifty different flags drooping in the heat.

After the politicians came the business men; after the business men, the underworld. By winking through your hotel window, you could buy yourself a lawyer, a woman or a long float, face down, in the sewers.

Dropped in the centre of town, outside the post office, Tyne slipped through the great undercover market, and headed up Bukit Besar. He entered the Merdeka Hotel. It seemed to him the obvious first place to look for Murray. The Merdeka had been the nearest equivalent to home for Allan, Tyne and Murray. They had grown to love its efficient service, its poor food, its constant bustle.

The place was full now, mainly with the sort of minor diplomatic staff Tyne had once been; nervous, cheery men downing their whiskies and keeping out of the sun—and waiting, waiting and watching. Pushing through the hall, Tyne went round the back way, to the back stairs.

He thought he saw Amir at the end of the passage, looking round and then dodging out of sight. But that could not be. Amir, the brightest boy on the staff, would have no reason to hide in that way; he had become almost a personal friend of theirs.

Climbing the back stairs, fishing his key out of his pocket as he went, Tyne reached Room Six. This was the room Allan, Murray and Tyne shared. Had shared . . . Unlocking the door, he went in.

The immense influx of foreigners had caused a housing shortage in Padang. Hotel rooms were impossible to find; only by paying through the nose for this one all the time did they enjoy the privilege of using it at weekends.

A hurricane had hit Room Six.

Tyne whistled. All their kit, their civilian clothes, everything, had been flung into the middle of the floor. Someone had searched the place, thoroughly, in a hurry. Who? Why?

"I don't like it," Tyne said aloud. He went and shouted over the banisters for service.

As he waited, he stood in the middle of the room, thinking. He was involved in a mystery. Something odd had happened on the moon—he had not heard the truth about that, he felt sure. Now something odd had happened here. Why had Murray deserted? Where had he gone? A numbing suspicion that he had murdered Allan overtook Tyne. But why?

He went back onto the landing and shouted for service again.

Hatred for Murray filled him. It reached back, embracing Murray-in-the-past. The big man's easy manner now seemed no longer likeable, but the sign of a boundless superiority. His ready, cheerful smile became false, the arbitrary grimace of a murderer. Yet supposing he had killed Allan . . . he could so easily have told Tyne that the Rosks had shot him—Tyne, after all, was unconscious when it happened. Nothing was sure. Rather, one thing was sure: Tyne wanted to get hold of Murray and wring the truth out of him.

He went out onto the landing to bellow for service again, and nearly bumped into a little maid.

"Where's Amir?" Tyne asked.

"Amir has a day off today."

"What? First time I've ever known him have a day off."

"Amir is not so well today. Has a bad head and takes medicine. What I can get for you?"

Suddenly, he wanted nobody to see into the room. He felt weak, tired, hungry; this was his first man hunt.

"Will you bring me some breakfast, please?"

"Breakfast is long finish, sir."

"Make it lunch then, anything."

Going back into the room, he locked the door on the inside. He started methodically tidying the muddle on the floor. It hurt to fold up Allan's belongings, knowing he would not want them again. Some of Murray's civilian clothes were missing, but a uniform was here. So.

Lunch came promptly, a denationalized dish of chopped sausages, cabbage and rice, followed by tasteless plankton jelly. A big new plankton plant down the coast at Semapang provided more and more food for the island; as yet, its products were more nourishing than appetizing.

With the meal, Tyne's spirits rose. He had ceased to be a second secretary to an under-secretary of the Under-Secretary because he wanted action. Here it came. The original instinct that had led him to Sumatra had been sound. He had been static, stale, discontented, a man without manhood, set on a career of his father's choosing that bored him thoroughly. His chief task had been minute passing; how suitable that that should be a synonym for time wasting!

But the equator is the hottest bit of the planet, the bit that goes round fastest, though that is not apparent to the senses. Now something was really starting to spin.

On his way out, he ran into the proprietor, and asked for Murray.

"Sorry, I don't see him today," Mr. Niap Nam said. "If he come, I don't see him. Now it is best you to leave by the back way. In front is having a little trouble from the Displaced. Maybe shooting from these foolish men."

"Thanks, Niap," Tyne said. He had heard the noise in the street but had taken no notice of it. In a moment, one shot was fired, the shouting rose to a crescendo, then came the sound of people running. Tyne slipped out the back way, through the courtyard, under the cassia tree. The Displaced were a group of terrorists, largely formed from natives whose kampongs had been evacuated to make room for the Rosk base; their daily acts of violence—often the sticky-bombing of diplomats' limousines—added an additional spice of risk to life in Padang.

Tyne headed for the Roxy. If anyone knew where Murray was, it should be Mina, the little half-Dutch girl (her other half remained unspecified) who occupied most of Murray's spare time. Tyne looked at his watch. It was just after noon; his enemy, for already that was how he thought of Murray, had as much as four and a half hours' start.

The Roxy was an all-day cinema. Now the boom was on, the solids flickered in the big perspex cube for twenty-four hours out of the twenty-four. The foyer was large, deep, lush, with people coming and going, or just standing smoking.

On the ice cream counter, Mina squeaked with pleasure at the sight of Tyne. Yes, she was nice: dark, lively, animated; perhaps after Murray was out of the way . . .

"Yes, he came to see me here," Mina said, in answer to Tyne's question. "Is he in some sort of trouble, Mr. Leslie, can you tell me? He had a look as if something is striking him not so funny."

"Perhaps he had his shoes on the wrong feet," Tyne said, and then waited patiently for the girl to control her shrieking laughter. He had forgotten how the silliest remark set her going.

"I've got to find him, Mina," he said. "The Commander wants him urgently. Did he say where he was going?"

"No, Mr. Leslie. All he say is not even 'give a kiss,' but just 'hello'. That is why I think perhaps something is striking him not—"

"Yes, not so funny. I know. What else did he say besides 'hello,' Mina? Did he ask you to meet him later?"

"Excuse a minute." She turned, all smiles, to serve a tall Pakistani, and then continued, "All he say to me is that he goes to the plankton plant. I can find him at the plankton plant. What for he wants to go to that place for, Mr. Leslie?"

"Perhaps to plant plankton," Tyne suggested, turning away unsmiling as she doubled up again with flutey laughter. What the devil would Murray be going out there for? Walking blindly, he almost bumped into a fat man in a white linen suit.

"Follow me to hear about Murray Mumford," the fat man said; speaking from the corner of his mouth and appearing to take no notice of Tyne. As Tyne stared after him in surprise, the fat man pushed through a swing door into one of the adjoining bars. For a moment, Tyne wondered if he had heard all right. Then he shouldered his way through the door.

A miniature solid a foot high fluttered on the bar counter. It was silent. Piped from the full-size cinema solid, it showed only half the original. As such, it was almost unintelligible: but its job was to lure bar-flies inside to see what the original was about. At present, the breasty half of Lulu Baltazar reclined on pillows gesturing meaninglessly.

Tyne flicked his gaze from the cube to the fat man. The fat man was sitting in the far corner with his face to the door, raising two plump fingers to the waiter. The waiter was nodding and smiling like an unctuous fool. Several people sat about, drinking.

"Who are you?" Tyne asked the fat man, on reaching his table. "Sorry, but I don't remember you."

"Sit down Mr. Leslie," the stranger said. "Remember your manners and thank your lucky stars I found you before anyone else did."

"Who are you, I asked?" Tyne said, sitting down. "Have you a message for me from Murray?"

"Here come the whiskies," the other said, smiling as the waiter set the glasses down. "Let me drink to your continued health."

Tyne pushed his away.

"I'm in a hurry," he said. "How do you know I am after Murray? I suppose you overheard what I said to the ice cream kiosk girl? Are you trying to be funny or helpful?"

The fat man downed his drink and then, looking quizzically at Tyne, usurped the one Tyne had pushed away. Without troubling to answer any of Tyne's questions, he said, "If you want to call me anything, Stobart is as good a name as any. I'm a U.N.C. agent. I can arrest you by flicking my fingers, should I feel like it."

A bit—a very nice bit—of Lulu Baltazar was climbing into a dynocar. The waiter was smiling and nodding like a fool to new patrons.

"You talk as if you've just popped out of a cloak-and-dagger solid," Tyne said.

"Don't reveal your genteel background, son," Stobart said curtly. "I'm real enough, as you'll find out if you start playing tough. And remember—I've got no sense of humour."

"All right. You're real," Tyne conceded. "Then tell me this. Why should a U.N.C. agent reveal himself as you have done? Why should he be interested in me, or in Mumford? If you were a thick-eared M.P. from camp, I could understand it."

"You couldn't understand a thick-eared hatstand. Look, son, you are dabbling on the edge of deep waters. Stay out. That's all I'm here to tell you; stay out! The finding of Murray Mumford is top priority, and you'll only be in the way of several interested parties."

As he spoke, he slid the whisky back to Tyne, who took it and drank it. Stobart raised two fingers in the air, and the waiter doubled over, curtseying, with more drink.

"Let me in on the mystery," Tyne said. He disliked the note of pleading he heard in his own voice. "Why did Murray kill Alan Cunliffe? Why are the U.N.C. and not the police or the Space Service after him?"

"You're inquisitive," Stobart said stonily.

Tyne went red in the face. He took one of the empty glasses in his left hand and squeezed. He went on squeezing till a little pile of glittering fragments lay on the table.

"Answer my questions," he said.

Stobart laughed. "You've got a temper," he said, and blew the powdered glass over Tyne's jacket. Before Tyne could move, the other had grasped his left wrist in an unshakeable grip.

"Listen to me, Mr. Leslie," Stobart said. "Stay out of this. Mumford lied to you, I don't doubt. He wouldn't let you see how big this thing was. I want to hear what he told you happened outside Area 101; then I'll tell you what really happened. Fair enough?"

Sullenly, Tyne repeated the story Murray had told him on the scout ship.

"Hogwash," Stobart exclaimed at the end of it. "While you were out cold on the moon, the Rosks *caught* you and Mumford. He had no time to get back into the ship, man, not with you sleeping peacefully on his shoulder. They caught him as easy as kiss your hand, and persuaded him to carry vital information down here, to a Rosk contact in Padang who will pass it to the Rosk Sumatra base."

"How could they persuade him? What was the information? Why couldn't he have told me the truth?"

"You innocent fool!" Stobart said. He had stopped looking at Tyne now, as if he had lost interest in him; his watery eyes slid round the other customers in the bar. "Do you think Mumford would tell anyone the truth? He has turned traitor! He's helping the Rosks; don't bother to ask me what they offered him for the job. And don't bother to ask me what the information is; if I knew I shouldn't tell you."

"I can't believe it! Why couldn't the Rosks carry the information themselves? They've got four small ships plying between Earth and Luna."

"If we knew all the answers, we'd not be looking for Mumford now," Stobart said tersely. "And that's all I've got to say to you. On your way, Leslie, blow. Go back to camp and play spacemen before the shooting starts."

"You're drunk, from the way you talk and look," Tyne said

91

quietly. "Or does your mouth always hang down like an old red sock?"

"There's a Rosk sitting up at the bar disguised as a Sumatran business man, watching us like a hawk," Stobart replied, without batting an eyelid.

"I'm from Neptune," Tyne said. "How did you get hold of all this information, Stobart?"

The fat man swore at him. "Think I'd tell you? For the last time, get, Tyne. You're up against organizations. You'll never find Murray Mumford. Go on, on your feet, beat it! The free whisky is finished."

A bit of someone was wrestling with a bit of Lula Baltazar as Tyne passed the bar. He boiled inside. His face burned. He hated every cubic inch of lard in Stobart's body, but his intelligence told him the man's advice was sound. If Murray was really involved in trouble so deeply, the affair had passed out of Tyne's hands.

Avoiding Mina's eye, he strode out onto the Roxy's steps. It was raining heavily. The streets ran with water. Further up the street, two miserable policemen stood beside a smoking Russian Pudenta; the Displaced had struck again. The time was 1.15.

Inside the cinema, Stobart watched with satisfaction as the Rosk agent slid from the bar and left, almost directly after Tyne Leslie. Stobart liked his job. As long as you stayed in control it was as comfortable as an old armchair. With the right psychological push, anyone could be induced to do anything. Even a random factor like Mr. Tyne Leslie.

III

Tyne decided to cut through the side streets. He might dodge most of the rain that way. The sooner he got back to base, the better; there would be trouble awaiting him for failing to report in from a completed mission. He felt full of defeat. He had even forgotten to ask that slob Stobart about Allan.

Rain pelted down his neck. His light tropical suit would be soaked in no time. A taxi slowly overtook him, splashing his legs.

"Jump in for a good ride, sir," the Chinese driver called cheerfully.

It was a sound idea. As Tyne bent to open the back door, it was flung wide. Strong hands grasped his hand, catching him off balance, pulling him into the car. He felt it gather speed even as he struggled under a heavy rug which was thrown over him. Someone was lying on top of him, pinning him down. Tyne fought to get his steel hand free. Then a blow caught him on the nape of his neck.

For what seemed like an eternity, he lay half-suffocating under the rug, in a drifting state between consciousness and unconsciousness. Lurid colours curled and coiled in his head. When the car began to bump, as if it had left the road, he took an intelligent interest in the world again. An odd hissing noise rose outside; they were driving through long grass.

The occupant of the back of the car had climbed off Tyne now, and was arguing with the driver. It was something about damage to the machine. Money was offered, the driver was refusing it.

At length the car stopped. Tyne did not struggle as his wrists were lashed behind his back. The hands that touched his felt feverishly hot. Undoubtedly their temperature was 105.1 degrees.

He was hauled unceremoniously out of the car by his shoulders, rolling over in knee-deep, wet grass. As he struggled to his knees, and then to his feet, he saw the Chinese driver accept a wad of dollars, grin and rev the engine. The Rosk took Tyne by the belt of his pants, pulling him out of the way as the car backed round and shot back up the track in the direction it had come from. It disappeared; man and Rosk were alone.

Tall trees, secondary growth rather than true jungle, surrounded them. The only sign of human existence was an old native hut sagging under its own weight, although in the distance came the regular sound of traffic; a highway not too far off.

"Let's walk, shall we?" the Rosk said, pleasantly, pushing Tyne ahead.

"If you've nothing better to offer."

It was still raining, but without passion, as they started down the track. Tyne had hardly managed to get a glimpse of his assailant. He looked like a Malayan. How ironic, Tyne thought, that this race should have set itself up in Sumatra! They could pass anywhere here unnoticed. In England, they would stand out a mile.

"Fond of the country?" Tyne asked.

"Keep walking."

The track grew worse. The rain stopped as if a celestial tap had been turned off. The sun came out; Tyne steamed. Through the trees, the ocean appeared. It lay there flat as failure, stagnant and brassy.

The cliffs were steep here, deep water coming in close. Together, Tyne and his captor slithered down a perilous slope. At the bottom, three great palms fought motionlessly for position on a minute ledge, their stony trunks canting over the water. Down below the surface, their roots extended like drowned fingers; Tyne could see fish among the fingers. Then, without warning, he was pushed off the ledge.

He went down among the roots, the water burning up his nose. He struggled frantically. He was drowning! With his hands tied, he was helpless.

There was hardly time to think. The Rosk was swimming beside him, tugging his collar. In no time, they slid into darker water

93

under the cliff, and surfaced. Water streaming from his mouth and clothes, Tyne gasped painfully, floundering up rough steps as the Rosk dragged him out.

They were in a cavern, the mouth of which would be hardly visible even from the sea, thanks to the big palms outside. Conditions were claustrophobic in the extreme. The water came within two-foot-six of the slimy roof; there was no chance of climbing out of the water—one just stood chest-deep in it. Bitterly, Tyne remembered that the Rosks had strong aquatic traditions.

In the middle of the cavern, in deeper water, floated a small submarine. It looked battered and ancient, and was streaked with rust. It might have been a veteran from the Malayan Navy, but Tyne could not certainly identify it.

The conning tower was open. A dark head now appeared, exchanging a few barked words with Tyne's captor. Without delay, he was prodded aboard.

Inside, it was like crawling round an oven, both as regards heat and size. Tyne was made to lie on the bare steel lattice of a bunk, his hands still tied behind his back. When the sub began to move, the motion was barely perceptible.

Shutting his eyes, he tried to think. No thought came. He only knew that the repulsive Stobart's warning had been well founded but too late. He only knew that he coveted the life of a second secretary to an under-secretary of the Under-Secretary.

"Up again now," the Rosk said, prodding his ribs.

They had arrived.

Pushed and goaded from behind, Tyne climbed the steel ladder and thrust his head into daylight.

The sub had surfaced out to sea. No land was visible, owing to haze which hung like a steam over the smooth water. A native, low-draught sailing ketch floated beside them, a mooring line from it already secured to the sub's rail. Three presumed Rosks showed predatory interest when Tyne appeared. Reaching over, they took him by the armpits and hauled him aboard, to dump him, dripping, on deck.

"Thanks," Tyne snapped. "And how about a towel, while you're feeling helpful?"

When his first captor had climbed aboard, he was urged down a companionway, still dripping. Below decks, structural alterations had created one good-sized room. The ketch was perhaps a hundred-tonner. Evidence suggested it had been used as a passenger boat, probably to nearby islands, before it passed into Rosk hands.

Five male Rosks and a woman were down here. They were dressed in Rosk style, with an abundance of oily-looking cloth over them that seemed highly out of place on the equator. Relaxed here, among their own people, the *foreign-ness* of them became more apparent. Their mouths, perhaps by the quick, clattering language they spoke, were moulded into an odd expression. Their gestures looked unnatural. Even in the way they sat on the plain wooden chairs was a hint that they found the artifacts alien, out of harmony.

These were beings from Alpha Centauri II, beings like men, but inevitably always estranged from man. The physical similarity seemed merely to mark the spiritual difference. As though life on Earth, Tyne thought, wasn't complicated enough without this . . .

The Rosk who had captured Tyne in Padang was delivering a report, in Roskian, to the leader of the group, a coarse-looking individual with nostrils like a gorilla's and a shock of white hair. He interrogated Tyne's captor at length, searchingly, but in a manner that suggested he was pleased with the man, before turning to address Tyne in English.

"So now. I am War-Colonel Budo Budda, servant of the Supreme Ap II Dowl, Dictator of Alpha-Earth. We need information quickly from you and shall use any means to extract it. What are you called?"

"My name is Pandit Nehru," Tyne said, unblinkingly.

"Put him on the table," Budda said.

Moving in unison, the other Rosks seized Tyne and laid him, despite his struggles, heavily on his back in the middle of the table.

"Pandit Nehru was a figure in your history," Budda said, impatiently. "Try again."

"Martin Todpuddle," Tyne said, wondering just what they did or did not know about him.

Evidently they did not know his name.

"You were talking to a U.N.C. agent," Budda said, "at half past twelve by your local time, in the Roxy Cinema, Padang. What were you talking about?"

"He was telling me I should change my socks more often."

A terrific side-swipe caught Tyne on his right ear. The world exploded into starlit noise. He had forgotten how unpleasant pain could be; when he reclaimed enough of his head to render hearing partly possible again, a lot of his cockiness had evaporated.

Budda loomed over him, gross, engrossed.

"We people from Alpha II do not share your ability for humour," he said. "Also, time is very vital to us. We are about to select from you a finger and an eye, unless you tell us rapidly and straightly what the U.N.C. agent spoke about to you."

Tyne looked up from the table at their foreshortened faces. What were these blighters thinking and feeling? How did it differ from what men would think and feel, in their position? That sort of basically important question had never been intelligently asked or answered since the Rosks arrived, nearly five years ago. The great, seminal, emancipating event, the meeting of two alien but similar races, had been obscured in a fog of politics. The merging of cultures boiled down to a beating-up on a table.

Tyne had been on the talking end of politics. Now here he was on the receiving end.

"I'll talk," he said.

"It's a wise choice, Todpuddle," Budda said; but he looked disappointed.

This acceptance of his false name gave Tyne heart again. He began a rambling account of the murder of his friend Allan, without saying where it took place.

Within a minute, the Rosk who had captured Tyne came forward, clattering angrily in Roskian.

"This fellow says you lie. Why do you not mention Murray Mumford?" Budda asked.

Turning his head, Tyne glared at his first captor. He had had no chance until now to get a good look at him. Like a shock, recognition dawned. This was the man drinking at the bar of the Roxy, whom Stobart had named as a Rosk agent; he was still dressed as a local business man. Then if Stobart knew this fellow, perhaps Stobart or one of his men was following, and already near at hand. Perhaps—that thought sent his flesh cold—Stobart was using him, Tyne as bait, expecting him to pass on Stobart's tale to the enemy. Stobart, at a rough calculation, was as callous as any three Rosks put together, even allowing two of them to be Ap II Dowl and Budo Budda.

His mind totally confused, Tyne paused.

At a barked command, one of Budda's henchmen began to rip at Tyne's clothes.

"All right," Tyne said. One look at Budda, crouching eagerly with tongue between teeth, decided him. "This is what Stobart said."

While they stood over him, he told them everything, concealing only the fact that he had been personally involved in the affair on Luna. As he talked, Budda translated briskly into Roskian.

On one point in particular the War Colonel was persistent.

"Stobart told you Mumford had to meet one of our contacts in Padang town, you say?"

"That's right."

"Mumford did not have to go to our base here?"

"I can only tell you what Stobart told me. Why don't you go and pick up Stobart?"

"Stobart is not so easily caught as you, Todpuddle. There is a native saying of ours that little fish are caught but big fish die natural deaths."

"Stuff your native sayings. What are you going to do to me?"

Budda did not answer. Going over to a cupboard, he opened it and pulled out a simple-looking gadget that evidently functioned as a radio phone. Something in his manner of speaking into it suggested to Tyne that he was addressing a superior, presumably at Sumatra Base. Interestedly Tyne sat up on the table; nobody knocked him flat again. The interrogation was over.

Replacing the instrument, Budda began shouting orders to the other Rosks.

Tyne slid his feet down onto the floor and stood up. His clothes were still wet, and clung to him. The cords that secured his hands behind his back seemed to grow tighter by the minute.

"Are we going home now?" he asked.

"You are going to your eternal home," Budda said. "You have served your function usefully, Mr. Todpuddle, and I am grateful. Now we all go to capture Mumford in a big hurry, leaving the lady of our party, Miss Benda Ittai, to sew you in a sack and hurl you in the blue water. It is an ancient Alpha form of burial. Farewell!"

"You can't leave me like this—" Tyne shouted. But the others were already hurrying up the companionway. He turned to face the Rosk woman.

He already knew she was beautiful. That was something he had noted instinctively on entering, although his mind had been on other things. Now he saw how determined she looked. Benda Ittai was small but wiry, very graceful despite her strange clothes, and she carried a knife—an Indonesian blade, Tyne noted.

She came towards him warily, clattering brusquely in her native tongue.

"Don't waste your breath, Mata Hari," Tyne advised. "I can't savvy a word of it."

He could hear the others climbing down into the sub; they'd be packed in there like kippers in a can, he thought. When they had gone, he could rush this little thug, knock her over, and get free.

But the little thing knew her onions. Bringing out an old sail from a locker, she spread it on the deck. Moving swiftly, she got Tyne in a sort of Judo hold and flung him down on top of the sail. Before he knew what was happening, he was rolled into its folds. Struggling was useless. He lay still, panting to listen. Benda Ittai was sewing him in—very rapidly, with an automatic needle. Right then, he really grew frightened.

When she had rendered him quite harmless, she went up on deck. In a minute, she was back, tying him round the middle with rope and thus dragging him, bump by bump, up the narrow stair well. The stiff canvas protected him from the harder knocks. When he reached deck level, Tyne began yelling for mercy. His voice was hopelessly muffled.

He was pulled across the deck to the rail.

Sweating, kicking feebly, he felt himself being lowered over the side. This is it, Leslie, he told himself in furious despair. He was swinging free. Then he felt the blessed hardness of a boat beneath him. The girl had put him into what seemed to be a rowing boat.

Tyne was still half-swooning with relief, when the girl landed beside him. The boat rocked gently, then shot away from the ketch. So it had a motor: but the motor was completely silent.

A momentary, irrelevant insight into the way Rosks got away with so much came to him. The average Sumatran is a very poor man. His horizon is of necessity bounded by economic need. The concept of world loyalty is not beyond him, but the chance to sell a fishing boat, or a knife, or a ketch, at a staggering profit is something which cannot be foregone.

To a considerable extent, the Rosks had found themselves on neutral ground. Power politics is a hobby the poor cannot afford. Absolute poverty, like absolute power, corrupts absolutely.

"I can help you in some way, Todpuddle," Benda Ittai said, resting her hand on the sail imprisoning Tyne.

By now, the situation was so much beyond Tyne, and to hear her speak English was so reassuring, that he could only think to mumble through his sheet, "My name's Tyne Leslie."

"The others of my party do not know I speak Earthian," she said. "I have learnt it secretly from your telecasts."

"There must be quite a bit about you they don't know," he said. "Let me out of this portable tomb! You really had me frightened back there, believe me."

She cut away at the canvas with her sharp knife. She would only make a hole for his face, so that he lolled in the bows like a mummy, staring at her.

Benda Ittai was as nervous as a courting mole.

"Don't look at me as if I am a traitor to my race," she said uneasily. "It is not so."

"That was not quite what I was thinking," he replied, grinning involuntarily. "But how do you come into the picture? What are you to do with Murray?"

"Never mind me. Never mind anything! All this business is too big for you. Just be content I do not let you drown. It is enough for one day."

The sea was still lake-calm. The mist still hung patchily about. Benda was steering by compass, and in a minute a small island, crowned with the inevitable palms, waded out of the blankness towards them. The girl cut the engine, letting them drift in towards a strip of beach lying between two arms of vegetation.

"I shall leave you here and you can take your chance," she said. "When Budo Budda returns to the boat, I tell him my duty is performed. Here the water is shallow enough. I will cut your binding and you will wade ashore. No doubt that a passing boat will soon see you."

"Look," he said desperately, as she severed the cocoon of sail,

98

"I'm very grateful to you for saving my life, but please, please, what is all this about?"

"I tell you the business is too large for you. With that, please be content."

"Benda, that sort of talk implies I'm too small for the business. That's bad for my complexes. You must tell me what's happening. How can this information Murray has be so vital that everyone is willing to commit murder to get it?"

She made him climb overboard before she would loosen his wrists, in case he pounced on her. He stood waist-deep in water. She tossed the knife to him. As he stooped to retrieve it, glittering like a fish under water, she called, "Your Murray carries what you would name a microfilm. On this film is a complete record of the imminent invasion of Earth by an Alpha fleet of ships. Our ship which arrived here five years ago is not what you think it is; your people were misled. It is only a forward, reconnaisance weapon, designed to make a preliminary survey for those who are now coming to invade. Against the slaughter to come, you or I, whatever we feel, can do nothing. Already it is really too late. Good-bye!"

Tyne stood in the sea helplessly, watching till she vanished into the golden mist.

IV

The solar system progressed towards the unassailable summer star, Vega. The Earth-Moon system wobbled round the sun, host and parasite eternally hand-in-hand. The planet spun on its rocky, unimaginable axis. The oceans swilled for ever uneasily in their shallow beds. Tides of multifarious life twitched across the continents. On a small island, a man sat and hacked at the casing of a coconut.

His watch told him that it was 4.20, local time. It would be dark in three hours. If the heat mist held till sunset his chances of being picked up today were negligible.

Tyne stood up, still chewing the last morsel of coconut flesh, and flung the empty case into the water. In a few minutes it drifted ashore again. He fumed at his own helplessness. Without the sun, he could not even tell in which direction Sumatra lay. There, wherever it was, the fate of man was being decided. If World Government could get hold of that precious spool of microfilm, counter measures could effectively be taken. Stobart had spoken vaguely of "information"; did he know the true value of what Murray was carrying? It seemed possible that Tyne was the only man in the world who knew just what tremendous stakes were in the balance.

Or did Murray know?

Murray had killed his friend and would betray his kind. What sort of a man was he?

"If ever I get my hands on him . . ." Tyne said.

He was determined that he would no longer be a pawn in the big game. As soon as possible, he would take the initiative. Unknown forces had hitherto carried him round, much as the revolving equator did; from now on, he would move for himself.

Accordingly, he made a tour of the island on which he had been marooned. It was not much more than ten acres in extent, probably an outlying member of the Mentawai group. On its far side, overlooking a tumbled mass of rock which extended far into the sea, was a ruined fortification. Possibly it dated from the Java-Sumatra troubles of the mid-twentieth century.

The fortification consisted of two rooms. In the inner one, a table rotted and an iron chest rusted. Inside the chest lay a broken lantern, a spade and a pick. Mildewed shelving lined one wall of the place.

For the next few hours, Tyne was busy building his own defences. He was not going to be caught helpless again.

As he worked, his brain ran feverishly over what the alien girl had told him. He was simultaneously appalled at the naivete of Earth in accepting as the simple truth the tale the Rosks had spun on arrival, and at the mendacity of Alpha II in thus taking advantage of man's generous impulses. Yet it was difficult to see how either side could have behaved differently. Earth had no reason to believe the Rosk ship was other than what it claimed to be. And if the Rosks were truly set on invasion, then from a military point of view their preliminary survey of Earth's physical and mental climate was indeed a sound one.

Exasperation saturated Tyne, as it so frequently had done in the old days round the U.N.C.'s shiny council tables. For these damnable oppositions, it seemed useless to blame the persons involved; rather one had to curse the forces that made them what they were.

After he had been working for an hour, a light breeze rose; the mist cleared, the sun shone. Low clouds in the horizon marked the direction of Sumatra. Tyne's clothes dried off, his mescahale lighter functioned again. He built himself a bonfire, lit it, and worked by its flickering radiance when the sun went down.

At last, his work completed, he flung himself down on the sand, overlooking the beach where Benda Ittai had left him. The light of one or two atomic freighters showed in the distance, taking no notice of his beacon. He slept.

When he woke, it was to cold and cramp. A chill wind blew. The time was only 9.40. Low over the sea, a segment of moon rose, cool and superb. And a fishing boat was heading towards the island.

Tyne was going to be rescued! At the sight of the reassuringly

100

familiar shape of a local boat, he realized how much he had dreaded seeing Budo Budda's ketch instead. At once he was jubilant.

"Here! Here I am! Help!" he called in Malayan, jumping up and flinging fresh wood onto his fire. The fishing boat moved rapidly, and was already near enough for the hiss of its progress over the water to be heard.

The boat carried a dim light halfway up its mast. Three men sat in it. One of them cried out in answer as they collapsed the single sail. The boat nosed in, bumping against the sand.

On his way down to meet them, Tyne paused. These men were muffled like Arabs. And one of them—that was a weapon in his hand! Alarm seized him. He turned to run.

"Stand still, Tyne Leslie!"

Reluctantly, he stopped and turned. Of the two who had jumped from the boat, one had flung back his hood. In the moonlight, his shock of white hair was dazzling, like a cloud round his head. It was War-Colonel Budo Budda. He was aiming his gun up the beach at Tyne.

They were not twenty yards apart, Budda and his fellow Rosk standing by the lapping sea, Tyne up the narrow beach, near the fringe of trees. It was a lovely night, so quiet you could hear your own flesh crawl.

"Is good of you to light a signal to guide us," Budda said. "We grew tired of searching little islands for you."

At the words, Tyne realized that their finding him was no accident. His heart sank still further as he realized that there was only one source from which they could have learnt he was still alive. Without thinking, he blurted out, "Where is Benda Ittai?"

Budda laughed. It sounded like a cough.

"We have her safe. She is a fool, but a dangerous one. She is a traitor. We long suspected it, and set a trap to catch her. We did not leave her alone on the boat with you, as we declared we would; secretly, a man was hidden to watch her. When she returned alone, having left you here he confronted her and overpowered her."

Whatever they had done to her, she had evidently not revealed where she had left him. That girl was a good one, Rosk or no Rosk. Tyne thought with compunction of her returning to the ketch, only to be jumped on. He remembered her nervousness; the memory seemed to come back to him like a fresh wind.

"You're too bloody clever, Budda!" he shouted. "You'll die of it one day."

"But not today," Budda said. "Come down here, Tyne. I want to know what the Ittai woman told you."

So that was why they did not shoot him outright! They needed to find out if Benda had passed on anything they did not know.

Without answering, he turned and ran up the beach, pelting for

101

the trees. At once he heard the sound of firing; the unmistakeable high-pitched hiss of the Roskian service gun, a big .88 with semi-self-propelled slugs. Then he was among the trees and the undergrowth, black, hunched, reassuring, in the dark.

He began immediately to double over to the left, on a course that would bring him rapidly back to the sea without leaving the shelter of the trees. As he dodged along, he looked frequently over his shoulder. Budda and companion were momentarily nonplussed; after the poor performance Tyne had made earlier in their hands, they probably had not expected him to show initiative. After holding a brief confab, they took a torch from the boat and commenced up the beach at a trot, calling his name.

By this time, Tyne had worked round to their flank. He crouched on a low cliff directly overlooking boat and beach. Groping in the undergrowth, he found three hefty stones.

At that moment, the two Rosks were running to the top of the beach. Tyne held his breath. They yelled together, their torch went spinning, they crashed into the trap he had prepared earlier on. To guard against eventualities, Tyne had used the spade he discovered to dig a deep trench in the sand across the path anyone heading inland would take. Covered with the rotted shelving from the old fortification, which in its turn was covered lightly with sand, it made a perfect trap. As the Rosks stepped on the concealed boards, they pitched through into the trench. Owing to the steep lie of the beach at this point, an avalanche of fine sand immediately poured in upon them.

Tyne's advantage could be only temporary, a matter of seconds at best.

As the Rosk in the boat stood up to see what the trouble was, Tyne flung the first stone at him. The man was clearly outlined against bright water, and only a few yards away. The stone struck his arm. He turned, raising a .88. A chunk of rock the size of a man's foot caught him in the stomach.

Almost as he doubled up, Tyne was down the sandy cliff and on top of him. He sprang like a leopard, knocking the Rosk flat. A clout over the head with another stone laid him out cold. Tyne pitched him unceremoniously out onto the wet sand, jumped out himself, and pushed the boat savagely out to sea. Flinging himself after it he climbed aboard and hoisted the sail. A bullet from the shore shattered the lamp on the mast. Tyne felt oil and glass spatter his flesh. He laughed.

Turning he saw two figures, black against the sand, climb out of his trap and run to the water. They fired again. The big bullets whined out to sea as Tyne dropped flat.

Rosks could swim like sharks. In their first year on Earth, before the trouble began, they had entered the Olympic Games and won all the aquatic events with ease. No doubt they could swim as fast as a fishing boat moving in a light breeze.

Fumbling into the bottom of the boat, Tyne's steel left hand found the gun dropped by the Rosk he had overpowered. He grabbed it with a whispered word of thanks.

Budda and his companion were wading out, still firing and clutching their torch. They made perfect targets. Steadying his aim over the side of the boat, Tyne drew a bead on the War-Colonel. The wind was taking the sail now, making the boat dip as it left the lee of the island. He tried to synchronize his firing with the motion, ignoring a hissing missile that slashed through a plank not a foot from his face.

It was funny to be trying to kill someone on such a grand night ... Now!

The Rosk weapon was superb. Recoil was non-existent. Across the level waters, not so many yards from the boat, Budda croaked once like a frog and pitched forward into the sea, carrying the torch with him.

"My God!" Tyne said. He said it again and again, as his boat gathered speed, dragging him over the moon-smeared waves. After the shock of killing came the exultation of it; he was almost frightened by the savage delight of his new mood. He could do anything. He could save the world.

The exultation quenched itself as he wondered where Budo Budda was now; whether anything of the Rosk survived apart from the body peering fixedly down into dark water. Then Tyne deliberately turned to face more practical matters.

Midnight was an hour and a half away. Time slid away from him like the wake of the boat. Murray had to be found before the Rosks reached him—unless he had been found already. Obviously, the first thing to be done on reaching the mainland was for Tyne to report all he knew to Stobart, or to someone in authority. To think to continue a lone hunt for Murray was foolish: yet Tyne found himself longing to do just that, to confront the monster, to ...

Yes, he wanted to kill the big, laconic space captain. Even—and it was shrinkingly he recognized the urge in himself—he wanted to feel that terrible exhilaration of killing for its own sake.

But another side of his nature merely wanted to solve the puzzle of Murray's disappearance and all that hung upon it. Merely! Tyne fumed to think he had been unconscious during those vital seconds in Area 101, of which Murray had given one account, Stobart another. The truth might lie in either or neither of them, and the truth might never be revealed. Truth was a primal force, almost like gravity; like gravity, it was always there, yet some people never even realized its presence.

Pocketing the .88 gun, Tyne steadied the high, stiff, tiller. One of his earliest memories, half embedded in the silt of forgetting, was of himself in his pram and certainly not more than three years old. He was throwing a toy out of his pram. The toy fell to the ground. Every time he threw it, the fool thing went *down*. He tried with other toys, with his shoes, his hat, his blankets. They all went down. He still remembered the disappointment of it. Even today, he still hated that lack of choice.

Truth had the same inevitability about it; he just had to go on throwing facts overboard and it would eventually reveal itself to him. This time it was worth persevering: the future of Earth hung upon it.

At the moment, it seemed to him almost an abstract problem. He knew he should be hating the Rosks, the five thousand of them here, the millions of them mustering back on Alpha II. Yet the hate did not work; could that be merely because he knew one of them to be both brave and beautiful?

He switched his attention to sailing. The sail was cumbersome, the boat did not handle readily. It would probably, Tyne reflected, take him longer to get back from the island to Sumatra than the scout ships took from Sumatra to Luna. Progress was a fever from which many parts of the world were immune; a thousand centuries on, and paddy fields would still be cultivated by hand. For a race set on attaining their blessings in the life to come, material innovation may be a complete irrelevance. Tyne, consequently, was going where the wind blew.

But he was lucky. A south-east monsoon wind had him. In half an hour, the coast was in sight. In another hour, Tyne was steering in under the dark cliffs, looking for a place to scramble ashore. On a small, rocky promontory, two native huts sagged under their load of thatch; a yellow light burned in one of them. Running the boat ashore on sand and stones, Tyne climbed out and made for the dwellings.

Among the trees stood a small kampong. It smelt good: smoky and sweet. Tyne found an old man, smoking the last half-inch of a cheroot in the moonlight, who would lead him to a road. As they walked, Tyne learnt with relief that he was no more than a dozen miles south of Padang.

"Not an hour's walking from here," the old man said, "is a telephone in which you may speak to certain people at the capital. If you say to them to send a fast car, a fast car will come."

"Thanks for the suggestion. I'll certainly do as you say. Whereabouts is this phone? In a house or a shop?"

"No, the telephone is in the new sea water works, where sea water is turned into food."

Tyne recognized this description; the old man was refering to the plankton plant at Semapang. He thanked him gratefully when they reached the road, asking him to accept the fishing boat as a present. Much delighted with this, the native in return produced some food wrapped in a palm leaf, which he insisted Tyne should have. Tyne thanked him and set off with a good heart. The folded leaf contained boiled rice, pleasantly spiced and with a few shreds of asswabi added. Tyne ate ravenously as he walked. Though the road was no more than a track, every rut in it lay clearly exposed in the moonlight. On either side stood the jungle, still as an English wood, forbidding as an English summer.

Fifty minutes passed before he gained the first sight of the plankton plant. By then, Tyne was feeling less fresh than he had done. The moon was inclined to hide behind accumulating cloud. Leaning against a tree, he paused to rest and consider. Thunder grumbled like thought above the treetops.

Mina, when Tyne questioned her in the Roxy, had said that Murray was coming here, to the plankton plant. The spy patrol captain could have only one reason for visiting this place. The plant was completely automated; at the most, it was peopled only by an odd engineer during the day and a guard at night. Murray must have chosen the spot as a hideout until he could make contact with his Rosk agent. On the face of it, it seemed a remote and unlikely spot to choose: but that in itself might be a good reason for choosing it.

Tyne's mind was made up. In his pocket was the Roskian .88 gun. He would hunt down Murray himself; if he was here, he would find him. There was a personal score to be settled with Murray. After that would be time enough to phone Stobart of the U.N.C.

Through the enamelled outlines of the trees, the bulk of the plankton plant loomed. It looked, in the wan moonlight like an iceberg. And like an iceberg, much of its bulk lay below water, for it stood on the edge of the sea, its rear facing onto land, its massive front thrusting out into the Indian Ocean.

Every day, millions of tons of sea water were sucked into its great vats, to be regurgitated later, robbed of their plankton content. These minute organisms were filtered into tanks of nutrient solution, fed and fattened, before being passed over to the synthesizing processes, which turned them into compressed food-stuffs, highly nourishing if barely palatable. Such plants, established at intervals round the shores of the Indian Ocean and the China Seas, had done much to alleviate the semi-famine conditions hitherto prevailing in the more populous areas of the tropics.

Tyne approached the place cautiously.

Though he had never been here before, he found it all familiar, thanks to the publicity it enjoyed. He knew that the plant was almost impossible to break into. Where, then, would a hunted man hide? One answer seemed most likely: on the seaward façade.

There, numerous arches and buttresses over the submarine

mouth of the plant would afford shelter from the elements—and from all but a personal, on-the-spot-search.

Now Tyne was going to make that search.

He slid round a deserted car park. Clouds drifted over the moon; he was happy to take advantage of them. At the end of the park was a high wall. Over the wall was a narrow passage, and then the main building, rising sheer. Carrying an empty oil drum across to the wall, Tyne stood on it, crouched, jumped upwards. Clawing desperately, he pulled himself on top of the wall. He crouched and listened. Nothing. Only the murmur of the sea, the stammering call of a night bird.

The impossibility of getting onto the building now dawned on him. The white walls rose a hundred and fifty feet above him, stretching away unbrokenly on either side, and punctuated only by a dark streak some yards away. Keeping his head down, Tyne wormed along the top of the wall; the dark streak resolved itself into a steel ladder, starting some fourteen feet above the ground and going right up to the roof.

Tyne, getting opposite to it, stood up on the wall and jumped forward, across the passage below. Seizing the rungs with both hands, he got a foothold. His steel hand was nearly wrenched from its socket with the sudden exertion; he clung there motionless until the pain in his arm had subsided. The darkness grew thicker and thicker while he waited. Thunder rumbled overhead. Then he began the upward climb.

Even as he started, the rain began. Tyne heard it swishing through the jungle towards him. Next moment, it hit him as if trying to squash him against the wall. He wondered grimly how long it was since he had last been completely dry and continued to climb.

Once on the roof, he squatted and peered about him, trying to see through the wet darkness. Raincloud now obscured the moon. To his right, he saw tall ventilation stacks and heard the rain drumming against them. He was cursing, half-aloud. He was cursing the whole universe, suns and moons and planets but especially planets, for harbouring freak phenomena like life and weather.

Advancing on hands and knees, he made for the seaward side. One last ridge to crawl up, one last ridge to slither perilously down, and he crouched on the top of the façade of the building. Below him were the arches and cavities in which he expected to find Murray. Below that, irritable now, lay the sea.

He could dimly see it, needled unceasingly by the downpour, sucking and slumping against the plant. Immediately below him was a patch of relatively calm water. This lay inside the plankton mesh, a vast perforated screen which ensured that nothing larger than a small shrimp would be sucked into the plant's internal processes. On the other side of the mesh, spray fountained.

In the noise about him, Tyne had lost the need for concealment. He stood up now and shouted, cupping his hands round his mouth. "Murray!"

The cry was washed away at once into the gutters of soundlessness. He did not shout again.

With water streaming down his face, Tyne dropped onto hands and knees, to begin a crawl along the leading parapet, looking for another inspection ladder that would enable him to get down the façade.

He found one. Grinning to himself with satisfaction, he swung his legs over the edge of the drop. As he took his first foothold, a shot rang out.

Tyne froze. He crouched with his head against the streaming concrete, body tensed against pain. It was impossible to tell where the shot had come from, from above or from below. For the space of ten unendurable seconds, he lay rigid. Then he slithered down the ladder as fast as he could go, heedless of the pain in his good hand and wrist. The wind buffeted him as he went.

No more shots sounded. But in the dark, someone was trailing him.

Tyne climbed off the ladder onto a narrow catwalk. Here was shelter. The architects responsible for the elaborate artificiality of this seaward façade had arched off this layer of it with a row of small, blind tunnels. If Murray was anywhere in the vicinity, the chances were that he would be here. As Tyne entered the first arch, a startled seabird clattered past his face, squawking. He stood quite still until his heart stopped jumping.

Then he began to move from one arch to the next, fumbling, looking for Murray. It was a nerve-racking business. Underfoot, a slippery mess of bird droppings made the going doubly perilous.

He had reached the third arch along when a watery moon slid through for a moment. Glancing back over his shoulder, Tyne saw a figure climbing down the steps he had just left. Man or Rosk? And if man: was it Murray? Acting hurriedly but indecisively, Tyne swung round to face his pursuer. His foot slid across the slippery concrete, went over the edge.

Before he could save himself, Tyne had fallen from the catwalk. For an instant, his ten fingers, five steel, five painfully flesh, scraped safety; then he was dropping freely, plunging down towards the sea.

Dark water slammed up to meet him. He hit it shoulder first and went under. As he came up gasping, he saw he was inside the plankton mesh.

Someone seemed to be calling from a long way off. The rain beat down like a solid thing, raising slashes from the sea, so that the surface was impossible to define. Tyne choked down water as

107

he swam for the wall.

Then over all the rest of the noise came a new one. It was low and continuous, the roar of a superhumanly angry bull. Tyne felt his legs caught, his progress halted, as if the sound itself had hold of him. He was being drawn underwater. Fighting, shouting, he realized what was happening. The plant's subterranean intake gates had opened. He was inside the screen. He was going to be turned into plankton juice.

Somewhere below him, sluices swung wide. The man was dragged under, over and over, swept into the throat of the great plant, helpless as a leaf in a storm. The last shreds of light and air were torn from his world.

V

The swamping pounding liquid registered on his tousled sense as sound: sound roaring him to death.

In the blundering blackness before Tyne's eyes, pictures squirmed like worms, sharing his agony. They were images of his past life bubbling up, scum-like, to the surface of his drowning brain. Incidents from his personal history returned to him, enfolding him as if to protect him from present pain. Then they were gone.

The bubble of the past had burst. His head was above water again. Exhaustedly, gulping down air, Tyne paddled to keep afloat in the racing water. Faint, reflected lights rode on the flood round him. He was somewhere inside the huge, automated plant, which was dimly lit by multi-coloured guide-lights here and there. The factory was cybernetically controlled, tenanted by robot devices. No one would save him if he could not save himself.

In his relief at finding his head above water, Tyne did not for a minute realize the grimness of his new predicament. He was simply content to float at the top of a rising tide of water, breathing and snorting painfully. Beyond thick glass, he could see the interior of the plant, where a shadowy file of processing tanks, moving by jerks, slowly revolved vats of jelly; endless pipes and presses marched into the background. He could see too, negligently, successive floors of the edifice sink from his gaze as the water lifted him up and up.

His mind snapped back into something like its normal degree of awareness. Searchingly, Tyne looked about. He had come up through the bottom of, and was now imprisoned in, a great glass tube with a diameter of some fifteen feet, standing a full six stories high.

Peering through the glass in sudden agitation, Tyne saw other giant tubes ranged alongside his, like the pipes of some overblown organ. The tubes stretched from base to roof of the plant, through all floors, and were filling rapidly with the incoming sea water.

Tyne looked up. The ceiling was growing closer. The tube was filling right up to the top.

This was inevitable. He knew immediately where he was. These entry tubes took each intake of water. When they were filled, great filter plungers came down from the top like slow pistons, filtering through the sea water, compressing plankton to the bottom of the tube: and not only plankton, but any other solid which happened to be there. Mercifully, Tyne Leslie would be dead by drowning before he was crushed against the bottom.

Between the turbulent water surface and the underside of the plunger, only some nine feet remained; the distance was decreasing rapidly.

Groaning, treading water, Tyne felt in his trouser pocket. The Rosk .88 was still there. Tearing it free, Tyne lifted it above the surface of the water.

Six feet left between him and the plunger.

He prayed that a man who had once told him that these weapons were unaffected by water had spoken the truth. Shaking it, he turned over onto his back, floated, aimed at the glass imprisoning him.

Five feet of air above him.

He squeezed the trigger. As always with this incredible weapon, there was no recoil. The big slug shattered the tube up, down and sideways, converting it in a flash into a multitude of glass shards, a foot thick and some of them a couple of stories long. Tyne was swept at this fearsome barrier by the weight of released water.

It carried him right out into the factory. For a moment, a great gulf extending down into the bowels of the plant hung below him. Then he snatched at and clung to a balcony railing. His arms creaked at their sockets but he clung there. As though for an age, Tyne hung on; as though for an age, water and glass cascaded past him, a waterfall containing death. With a great effort, he climbed over the rail to safety, hardly realizing himself alive.

Another sound roused him, a sound easy to identify: a siren was wailing; directly he punctured the big tube, an automatic alarm had gone off.

To be caught in there would mean the end of everything. Forfeiting his freedom might mean losing the last chance of finding Murray, even the last chance of passing the vital information gained from Benda Ittai on to the proper authorities. Tyne got up, dripping, pushing the wet hair back from his eyes. He was on a catwalk; a couple of feet away, crates of processed plankton, now disguised as steaks and pastes and spreads, moved briskly on a conveyor belt. And rapid footsteps sounded near at hand.

The dark was penetrated by widely spaced lights, some red,

some orange, some blue. Peering through the gravy blackness in which swabs of light swam. Tyne saw a figure running round the catwalk towards him. Two figures! Whoever had pursued him outside, had managed to follow him into here. Someone with keys to the place.

"Leslie! Tyne Leslie!" a voice called.

It was magnified, distorted, made metallic, by the acoustics of the building; Tyne did not think he would have recognized it, even in more favourable circumstances. With sudden fear, he felt convinced that the Rosks were after him. He jumped onto the conveyor belt.

He slipped, knocking a crate off the other side; the belt was travelling considerably faster than he had estimated. In some alarm, Tyne knelt up, staring back to see where his pursuer was. At that moment, he himself was borne under an orange light. Cursing lest he had given himself away, Tyne turned to see where he was being carried.

A low entrance loomed just ahead.

Involuntarily, Tyne shouted with alarm. He ducked. At once, impenetrable darkness swallowed him. He was in a tunnel. His elbow hissed against a moving side wall, and he tucked it in hastily. He dared not raise his head. There was nothing to be done but crouch between crates.

The conveyor emerged suddenly into a packing bay. A robot loader under a bright light was pushing the crates from the belt into waiting trucks, whose doors slammed shut when they filled. This was not for Tyne. He rolled off the belt just before the robot got to him.

There was not time to choose how he was going to drop. He fell painfully flat on the floor, picking himself up slowly and wearily. His watch told him that it was nearly 3.30 a.m. He should be in bed and asleep. He ached all over.

Even as he got to his feet, the conveyor exit ejected his two pursuers. They, apparently, knew better than Tyne what to expect; as they catapulted into the packing room, they jumped clear one after the other, landing nimbly on their feet. Before Tyne could make up his mind to move, they had collared him.

"Come on, Leslie; let's get you out of here," one of them said, holding tightly onto his arm.

They were masked.

Tyne could see nothing of their faces beyond their forehead and their eyes, which looked at him over the top of knotted hand-kerchiefs.

"Who are you?" he asked feebly. "Why the yashmak effect?"

"Explanation later," one of the men said. "Let's concentrate on getting you out of this building before half Padang arrives to investigate that alarm."

The siren was still shrilling as the men led Tyne down a couple of floors, unlocked a door with a special key, and pushed him into the open. At an awkward jog trot, they hurried down a slope, their way intermittently lit by lightning. Although rain still fell, its force was hesitant now; the storm had worn itself out. Water gurgled down into storm drains beside their path.

A door stood at the end of the passage. The burlier of the two men, evidently the one in authority, produced another key, unlocked the door and flung it open.

They emerged behind an almost deserted car park, not far from the point at which Tyne had first tackled the building. Trotting across the puddle-strewn ground, they ran to an ancient model of a Moeweg, a German atomicar. Burly flung himself into the driver's seat as the others bundled into the back. He jerked the dipstick and they were moving at once.

As they accelerated past the front of the plant, the first car to answer the alarm call arrived from the opposite direction. It had a searchlight mounted on the roof; it was a police car. As the old Moeweg dashed by, a uniformed man leant out of the police car and bellowed to them to stop. Burly accelerated.

"Damn it, they'll have our number," he said over his shoulder, to the man beside Tyne. "We'll meet trouble as sure as eggs. I'm going to turn off before we hit traffic; this is no time to play questions and answers with a bunch of local cops."

A fire engine dashed past them. A helicopter thundered overhead. Bright headlights through trees indicated a stream of traffic heading round a bend for the scene of the alarm. Burly wrenched the dip; they slewed across the road and squealed into a narrow lane leading into jungle.

The lane had been intended for nothing bigger than a cow-cart. Foliage whipped and smacked against the windows as the car lunged forward.

It's crazy! Tyne thought, all absolutely crazy! He had time to wonder about the respect he had held for men in action. He had seen them as people at the equator of life, in the hottest spots, going round the fastest; he saw now it was true only in a limited sense. These people merely went in circles. One minute they were hunters, the next hunted. They made decisions rapidly, yet those decisions seemed based less on a rational understanding and interpretation of their opponent's motives than on a desire to keep hopping continually in an immense indeterminate game.

A game! That was the secret of it all! These men of action could enter a contest involving life and death only because once they had plunged in, the stakes became unreal. This was chess, played with adrenalin instead of the intellect. They had got beyond the ordinary rules of conduct.

The terrible thing was, Tyne found, that although he now saw

111

this clearly enough, he too was caught in the game—voluntarily. World events had become too grave to be treated seriously. One could escape from all their implications by sinking into this manic sub-world of action, where blood and bluff ruled. By the same token, he saw the pendulum which ruled the sub-world sliding back in his favour. These men had caught Tyne when he was unprepared; now that he was in their hands, he could be relaxed but alert; in a sense, he had no care; they had the worries. When this pressure grew to a certain pitch, they would become in their turn unprepared—and he would elude them. It was inevitable, just a rule in the crazy game. After that, of course, the big pendulum would swing the other way again . . .

"This is far enough," Burly said, when the Moeweg had rocked and staggered some hundreds of yards into the jungle. The man beside Tyne never uttered a word.

The car stopped, and with an effort Tyne brought his attention back to the present. His mind had been busily elaborating his theory—even giving it some such half-jocular title as Leslie's Principle of Reciprocal Action, or the Compensatory Theory of Irresponsible Activity ("Leslie's Effect")—with the same attention it had once devoted to preliminary drafts of official memoranda.

Burly flicked off the headlights, so that only the dash light illumined them. Outside, the rain had stopped, though the foliage overhead still dripped meditatively onto the car roof. It was 4.15, a numb, light-headed time of night.

"All right," Tyne said, "now suppose you tell me who you are, what you're doing, and why you think you're doing it?"

Removing the cloth which had covered the lower part of his face, Burly turned in his seat to look at Tyne.

"First of all," he said, in a gentle, educated voice, "we ought to apologize for virtually kidnapping you like this, Mr. Leslie. Time pressed, and we had no alternative. I ought perhaps to add —forgive me—that none of this would have been necessary if you had waited for us to explain when we caught you up on the façade of the plankton plant. Your dive into the sea was spectacular, but unnecessary."

"I didn't dive," Tyne said, wryly. "I slipped."

Abruptly, Burly burst into laughter. Tyne found himself joining in. The tension eased considerably. The masked man beside Tyne never moved.

"This is the situation," Burly said. "My name, by the way, is Dickens—Charles Dickens. No relation, of course. I am working with the man you know as Stobart, the U.N.C. agent; his second in-command, as it were. You have been missing now for some hours, and we frankly were worried. You see, your role in this affair is an ambiguous one; we naturally like to know where you are."

112

"Naturally. What made you look for me at the plankton plant?" Tyne inquired. "Or shouldn't I ask?"

"We weren't looking for you," Dickens said. "We just happened to be searching the place at the time you came along. Like you, we were hoping to find Murray Mumford there."

"How did you know I was still looking for Murray?"

"You called his name, remember? For another thing, Mina, Murray's woman, told you to go there. *She* told you Murray had said he would be at the plankton plant."

Tyne suddenly fell silent. Dickens' words brought back a vital memory to him, something that he had recalled during those terrible moments of drowning in the plant. The memory gave him the key to Murray's whereabouts; he must get away from Dickens and his silent partner as soon as he had as much information as possible from them. Dragging his mind back to the present, he asked, "How did you find out about Mina, Dickens?"

"Stobart found out. He questioned her after you'd left him. We've not been sitting down doing nothing."

"Don't talk to me about Stobart. There's a man who should learn a few manners before he mixes with people."

"Stobart is something of a psychologist," Dickens said. "He deliberately made his advance to you to stop looking for Murray so unpalatable that you would ignore it."

Tyne smiled to himself. These boys thought they had all the answers. What they did not know was that he had, in fact, already stopped looking for Murray when the Rosk picked him up in the taxi. Stobart could stuff that up his psychology.

"So Stobart wanted me as a stooge," he said. "Why?"

"You were just one of his impromptu ideas. The Rosks had him cornered in the Roxy when you arrived. You were a diversion to draw them away. Actually, you were doubly useful. After the Rosks had taken you out to their ketch—"

"What!" Tyne exploded. Suddenly he was furiously angry. The silent man beside him placed a restraining hand on his arm, but Tyne knocked it off with his steel fist. "You mean you people know about that ketch? Yet you let it stay there? You let me be tortured—well, I was nearly tortured there. You let that thug of Ap II Dowl's, Budo Budda, come and go there as he pleased? And all the time you *knew* about the ketch and could have blown it out of the water? Isn't it infringing the interplanetary agreement merely by being there?"

"Don't get excited. We didn't know you were taken to the ship; the Rosks picked you up too quickly for that—you weren't half awake, Leslie! We were waiting for big game; Ap II Dowl is to visit that ketch in the early hours of this morning. By now, in fact, we should have trapped him there. If we can get him in the bag, many of Earth's troubles will be over."

"You don't know how many troubles she's got," Tyne said grimly. "She is about to be attacked by an Alpha II invasion fleet. That's the cheering news Murray carries round with him."

"We know."

"You know! How do you know?"

"We have means, Mr. Leslie; leave it at that."

As Dickens spoke, a buzzer sounded. A radio phone was installed on the Moeweg's dashboard, Dickens picked it up, listened, spoke into it in a low voice; Tyne caught his own name being mentioned.

"Can't you ever think of a word to say?" he asked the man sitting next to him. The other shrugged his shoulders and made no answer.

Suddenly Dickens thrust the phone down and swore luridly. He cursed with vigour and a vinegary wit, making it as obscene as possible. It was a startling display, coming from him.

"Leslie, you've properly buggered things up," he said, swinging round in the car seat. "That was Stobart calling. He says you were marooned on a small island called Achin Itu until about ten o'clock this evening—that is, yesterday evening. They found your monogrammed mescahale lighter on the beach. Is that a fact?"

"I'd like that lighter back; it cost me fifty chips. Tell Stobart, will you?"

"Listen, Leslie, you shot up that Rosk Colonel, Budda. Do you know what you've done? You scared Ap II Dowl away! When he got wind of Budda's death, he stayed tight in the base. Our fellows raided the ketch an hour back, while you were playing tag over the plankton plant, and got nothing but a lot of useless information."

"Don't blame me, Dickens. Call it one of my impromptu ideas, eh? Any time one of Stobart's plans go wrong, give me the word; I find I get a thrill out of hearing about it."

"You're coming back to Padang with me, Leslie, right away. We're going to lock you up until you learn not to make a nuisance of yourself."

"Oh, no you don't!" Tyne said, half-getting out of his seat. Something hard pressed against his side. He looked down. The silent partner was digging in with a revolver, his eyes unwavering above the handkerchief. Dickens switched the car headlights on again as Tyne sat back helplessly in his seat.

"That's right, relax," Dickens said. "From now on, you're living at the government's expense."

"But I've got a hunch about finding Murray," Tyne said. "I swear to you, Dickens, I may be able to go straight to him. You still want him, don't you?"

"We'd trade in the U.N.C. Building for him," Dickens said quietly, starting the engine. "But things are too complex for you, feller. There's no room outside for amateurs just at present; you've

114

done enough damage. Here's another thing you didn't know. Have you paused to wonder why the Rosks couldn't slip a roll of microfilm smaller than your little finger from Luna to Earth themselves? There's a reason why they got Murray to carry it. It's stolen from the Rosks."

"You mean the Rosks stole the film from the Rosks?"

"Yes; that's what I said and what I mean. Ever heard of the Roskian peace faction, the RPF, led by Tawdell Co Barr? They're a small and semi-illegal organization of Rosks ranged against Ap II Dowl and pledged to work for peace with Earthmen. Their numbers are few. In Luna Area 101 there can't be more than a handful of them. But they managed to get their hands on this film, and of course they want it to reach the main body of RPF in the Sumatran base here. I fancy it'll be used for propaganda purposes, to show the Rosks what a bloody-thirsty maniac Dowl is.

"I tell you this so that you can see why the situation is too complex for you; it comes in layers, like an onion."

Even as he spoke, Dickens was wrestling with the car. The wheels spun in mud but did not move. While they waited here for the alarm on the main road to die down, the heavy vehicle had sunk into the soft track. Tyne scarcely noticed what was happening as he mulled over what Dickens had told him. It threw new light on at least one Rosk: the girl, Benda Ittai, who had saved his life.

"Have you ever heard of Benda Ittai?" Tyne asked. Speaking her name aloud filled him with an unexpected pleasure.

"We're bogged down, damn it," Dickens said. "Oh, how I love Sumatra! Benda Ittai is evidently one of the RPF. Stobart's men found her on the ketch when they raided it. The Rosks were about to put her to death. Under the circumstances, our men found it best to let her go free; I tell you, Stobart has a soft heart—I'd have locked her up. Damn this filthy, soggy country! I can understand how they get volunteers for lunar duty. Yes, if I had my way, I'd clap her in prison; I'd clap all of you—look, I'm getting out to put something under the wheels. Leslie, if you try to escape, my friend will shoot you in the leg. It's painful. Do by all means try it and see."

He climbed out, leaving his door swinging open. His feet squelched in the wet grass, and he steadied himself against the Moeweg's bonnet.

Tyne's heart thudded. He wondered if he stood a chance of overpowering the fellow beside him. Dickens was visible through the windscreen, bathed in bright light which only emphasized the sad, waiting, darkness of the forest on either side. The agent had produced a small sheath knife and was hacking at the thick fronds of a bush, throwing them under the car's front wheels.

Then something else was moving out there. It came swishing in from the treetops with a vibrant humming. Bushes and twigs

115

writhed and cringed; everything seemed to turn live at its approach.

Dickens straightened and saw it. Beautifully in control of himself, he dropped the foliage he had cut and reached for a holstered gun without a second's pause. As his hand came up, he fired two shots at the thing, then turned and leapt into the Moeweg, slamming the door shut behind him. Furiously, he made a fresh attempt to extricate the car from the mud. The flying thing charged at them, bowling in from the bending darkness.

"What is it? What the devil is it?" Tyne asked, severely rattled. He began to sweat. His ears jarred with the noise the thing made.

"It's a Rosk fly-spy," Dickens said, without turning his head. "Sort of flying eye. Televises reports of all it sees back to Rosk base. I've seen a captured one back at H.Q. They're unarmed but definitely not harmless. Mind it doesn't—ah!"

They jerked forward a foot, then fell back again, their wheels failing to grip. The fly-spy hovered, then dropped almost to ground level. Tyne saw it clearly now. It was a fat disc, perhaps five feet in diameter and two feet six at its greatest width. Lenses of varying size studded its rim and under-surface. An inset searchlight swivelled a blinding beam of light at them.

Rotors, probably mounted on a gyroscope, powered the machine. They set up the humming note, making the bushes in their vicinity move uneasily, as if trying to escape observation. The rotors were set inside the disc, protected by fine mesh from possible damage.

It moved forward suddenly. Even as Dickens instinctively ducked, the fly-spy struck their windscreen, shattering it into tiny fragments. Dickens swore ripely.

"The Rosk base isn't far from here!" he shouted. "Just a few miles through the jungle. If this thing has identified us, it may be planning to wreck the car—to hold us up till a Rosk patrol can get at us. Cover your face up, Leslie—don't let it see who you are!"

The fly-spy had lifted. It hovered somewhere above the vehicle. They couldn't see it, but they could hear it, the venomous note of a hornet, amplified. All the leaves near the car waved furiously, enduring their own private storm. Tyne was tying a handkerchief round his face when Dickens flung the engine into reverse. Bucking wildly, the old Moeweg heaved itself out of the pit it had gouged for itself. At once the fly-spy returned to the attack. With a slicing movement, it sped down and struck one of the rear side windows. It did not retreat, just stayed there pushing, huge through the shattered glass, its lens seeming to sparkle with malice. The car lurched, the coach-work crumpled.

The silent agent scrambled up onto the seat, taking pot shots through the broken window. His forehead was grey and patchy above his mask.

"Aim at its rotors through the mesh!" Dickens bellowed.

116

"That's the only way you'll knock it out!"

They were speeding recklessly backwards down the jungle track. Dickens drove looking over his shoulder, dipstick in one hand, gun in the other.

"That thing can squash you if you try to run for it," he said. "Squash you flat against the ground."

"I wasn't planning to jump out," Tyne replied. He had just been planning to jump out.

As he spoke, the silent man flung open his door, hanging out to get a better shot into the middle of the fly-spy's works. The thing reared up immediately into the branches overhead—and crashed down into one of the back wheels. The Moeweg skidded sideways into bushes and stopped, engine bellowing uselessly.

Tyne hardly paused to think. He knew they were trapped now. This thing could batter the car apart if it was so directed.

The dumb agent had been pitched onto the ground by the skid. Leaping through the open door, Tyne jumped onto him, snatched his gun and plunged into the undergrowth. He dived into the bushes recklessly, doubled up, doing anything to get away. Moving on hands and knees, he charged forward, heedless of any cuts or tears he sustained. Shots sounded behind him; he did not know if Dickens was firing at him or the fly-spy.

He travelled fast. He tumbled into a little overgrown stream and was out in a flash. The faintest light, perhaps the first light of dawn, aided him.

He knew what to do. He was heading for a belt of thick trees with low branches. The fly-spy had severe limitations, for all its power. Dense foliage would stop it.

Tyne was on his feet now, running doubled up. He no longer knew which way he was running. That deep, determined humming sounded behind him. A light flickered and swam among the leaves, as the searchlight sought him out. The leaves writhed. Where were the damned trees?

Blowing hard, he pounded through chest-high vegetation. It seemed endless.

Now he bounded down a bushy slope, plunged into a line of trees, tore himself free of brambles. When he tripped a minute later, he could hardly get up. Looking wearily about his head, he saw against the dark sky a protecting network of branches. The smaller branches waved in an artificial wind.

Panting, Tyne lay there like a trapped animal.

All he could do, he had done. He hadn't imagined it would come after him; he had thought it would stay by the car and the two U.N.C. agents. But . . . if its transmissions back to Rosk base had caused him to be identified there as the Earthman to whom Benda Ittai had spoken, then there was good reason for his being the quarry.

117

The leaves and grasses trembled about him. The resonant hum filled his ears. Jumping up like a frightened stag, Tyne flung himself into one of the trees. Pulling himself up, he hauled himself ten, fifteen feet above ground, hugging the trunk among a welter of stout, out-thrusting branches.

Seeing was better now. First light drifted like sludge through the trees. The slope he had run down lay in one direction, a fast river in the other. On the other side of the river lay what looked like a track.

The fly-spy had seen him. It swooped in low, cutting above the ground, its light probing. It could not rise to him because of the branches; they shielded him as he had hoped. Instead, the machine nuzzled lightly against the tree bole. For the first time, looking down on it. Tyne saw its big fans, revolving in a whirl behind protective gratings. He fired at them with the agent's gun. His arm shook, the shot went wild.

The machine backed away and butted the tree. Then it circled out, seeking another way to get at him. Almost at the same time. Tyne became aware of Dickens, running down the slope. Following the fly-spy's noise, the agent had followed Tyne.

Branches cracked. The fly-spy was pushing through twigs and light branches on a level with Tyne. Tyne slid round the other side of the trunk. If he could only hold out till full daylight, this thing would be bound to go home or else risk detection. He squinted down below, but Dickens had disappeared.

Again he changed position, to keep the tree's girth between himself and the machine. This meant slipping down to a lower branch. He must beware of being forced all the way down; on the ground he was defenceless. The thing droned angrily, like an immense spinning top, pushing persistently through a maze of twigs. It worked to one side; again Tyne worked away from it.

Suddenly there was a shout, and the sound of shoes kicking steel.

Tyne looked round the tree, peering out like a scared squirrel.

Dickens had jumped or fallen onto the fly-spy! The agent had climbed the next tree and then launched himself or dropped outwards. Now he sprawled on top of the disc. fighting to get a grasp of it.

"Dickens!" Tyne yelled.

The agent slithered over the rocking surface of the fly-spy. His legs dangled, kicking wildly in air. Then he caught a finger hold in the machine's central mesh and drew himself into a more secure position. As the fly-spy rocked among the branches, he pulled his gun out, aiming it at the rotor blades.

All this had obviously taken the Rosks who controlled the big disc completely by surprise. It just drifted where it was, helplessly. Then it moved. Its pervasive note changing pitch, it shot up like

118

an express lift.

Dickens was knocked flat by a bough. Partially stunned, he slithered once more over the side, and his gun went flying—clatter-clattering all the way from branch to branch down to the ground.

"Jump, Dickens, for God's sake!" Tyne shouted.

It was doubtful if the agent heard a word of it. He was carried up through the foliage, hanging on grimly, head half-buried in his arms. The last leaves swished by, and the fly-spy was out in the open, climbing slowly.

Heedlessly, Tyne jumped from the tree to sprawl full length in a flowering bush. Picking himself up, he broke from the trees, running along below the fly-spy, shouting incoherently. He dared not fire in case he hit Dickens.

In the vapid early morning light, the disc was clearly visible thirty feet up, heading fast on an unswerving course that would, Tyne guessed, take it back to Sumatran Base, where the Rosks awaited it. Dickens had evidently had the same thought. He knelt on top of the thing, wrenching at the screens on its upper surface. In a moment, he had unlatched a segment of screen, a wedge-shaped bit that left the rotors revolving nakedly underneath.

He wrenched his shoe off and flung it into the rotors.

At once the dynamic hum changed into a violent knocking. From the knocking grew the mirthless squeal of metal breaking up. With a few staccato grinding sounds, the fly-spy began to fall, canting sharply.

Tyne was still running when it crashed into the river he had noticed earlier, bearing its passenger with it. They disappeared with a splash and did not come up again.

VI

It was 9.15 in the morning.

Tyne Leslie sat at the back of a Chinese coffee shop, eating durian off a cracked plate. His cheeks were smooth, his head was clear; he had been to a nappi wallah who had shaved him and massaged his head and shoulders. When he had finally plodded into Padang ninety minutes ago, after a fruitless search along the river bank for Dickens, he had felt half-dead. Now he was, after the shave, the massage and breakfast, alive again, alert, planning ahead, casting little feelers of worry into the future.

Already he had written a note to Under-Secretary Grierson, a second secretary to whose under-secretary Tyne had been, outlining the threat of invasion to Earth. That note had been delivered to the British Diplomatic Mission building, and would be before the Under-Secretary himself within an hour. How long it would be before any action was taken on it was another matter.

Meanwhile, time grew short. Murray had been at large in Padang for twenty-four hours. If the Roskian RPF agent had been unable to reach Murray, it would be because he had been dogged by his own people, the Rosks faithful to Ap II Dowl. Undoubtedly though, the parties interested in finding Murray were closing in: RPF, Dowl's men, the U.N.C., and possibly—undoubtedly, if they had wind of the affair—various nationally interested Earth groups. And Tyne.

And Tyne. He had told Dickens he was prepared to go straight to Murray. It was the truth. By a paradox, he could have done as much yesterday, before Stobart spoke to him.

The truth had lain, as so often happens, inside him, waiting for the ripe moment to reveal itself.

When Tyne questioned Mina in the Roxy foyer, she said that Murray had announced he was going to the plankton plant. She had assumed—and Tyne had unthinkingly accepted her assumption—that Murray meant the plant at Semapang, where he had nearly drowned himself. When Stobart had questioned the girl later, he had got the same answer; that was why Tyne and Dickens had met at the building.

But Murray had meant something quite different when he spoke of the plankton plant.

In those terrible seconds when Tyne was dragged drowning through the submarine intakes at Semapang, scenes from his past life had bubbled through his mind. One scene had been of Murray, Allan Cunliffe and himself breakfasting at the Merdeka Hotel after a heavy night. While he and Allan sat drinking coffee, Murray tucked in to a large breakfast, complaining all the time about the badness of the food. "It's always synthetic at the Merdeka," he said. "Doesn't matter what the food resembles, it's really plankton underneath. As the Americans say, it's a plant. A planton plant! I tell you dreary-looking couple of so-and-sos, we live in a plankton plant. Before you know it, the management will be offering us plankton women . . ."

The comments had stuck. From then on, the three of them had occasionally referred to the Merdeka as "the plankton plant"; it had been a private joke between them, until they tired of it.

All of this had run through Tyne's drowning mind. He knew now that to find Murray he had to go to the Merdeka again; that was the place Murray had been referring to. Mina had been misled; so had Stobart; naturally enough, for they had never heard the old private joke. Tyne had been once, fruitlessly, to the Merdeka; today, he was going to ask the right questions of the right people.

Settling his bill, he left the café. He had already purchased a spare clip of ammunition for the stolen gun in his pocket. Now he moved through side streets, warily, alert for danger. A protest march of the Displaced, complete with drums and banners

120

("ROSKS LEAVE OUR WORLD TO PEACE," "WORLD POWERS ARE
DUPES OF ALIENS," "SUMATRA HAS BEEN SACRIFICED!"), acted as
convenient cover as Tyne slipped into the foyer of the hotel.

The familiarity, at once welcome and repugnant, of the place
assailed him like a pervasive fog. At this hour, before Padang's
political life, with its endless conferences and discussions, was
under way, the lounge was full of the sort of men Tyne had been:
restless, wretched (but smiling!) men who continually manoeuvred,
but never manoeuvred boldly enough. Tyne skirted them, feeling
as alien to them as a Rosk might have done.

He went through the building into the rear courtyard, where
two very ancient Chinese ladies were combing each other's hair in
the sunshine.

"Have you seen Amir, please?" Tyne asked.

"He is at the warehouse, checking the rations."

The "warehouse" was a crude brick shed beyond the courtyard,
tucked between other buildings and conveniently facing a small
back lane. Outside it stood a little delivery van labelled, in
Malayan, Chinese, Russian and English, "Semapang Plankton
Processed Foodstuffs". The Merdeka was getting its daily quota
of nourishment.

As Tyne approached, a uniformed driver emerged from the
warehouse, climbed into the van and drove off. Tyne went stealth-
ily to the warehouse door. Amir was there alone, left arm in a sling,
leaning over a box checking delivery notes. Tyne entered, closing
the door behind him.

Amir had been something of a friend of Allan's and Tyne's.
Now there was only fear on his dark, intelligent face as he looked
up and recognized his visitor.

"What have you done to your arm, Amir?"

"I thought you were dead, Mr. Leslie!"

"Who told you that?"

"You should not be here! It is dangerous here, Mr. Leslie! The
Merdeka is always being watched. Please go away at once. For
everyone's safety, go away!"

His agitation was painful to watch. Tyne took his good arm and
said, "Listen, Amir, if you know there is danger, you must know
something of what is happening. The lives of everyone on Earth
are threatened. I have to find Murray Mumford at once. At once!
Do you know where he is?"

To his surprise and embarrassment, the young Sumatran began
to weep. He made no noise or fuss about it; the tears rolled down
his cheeks and fell onto the clear floor. He put up a hand to cover
his eyes.

"So much trouble has been caused my country by other
countries. Soon I shall join the Displaced. When our numbers are
big enough, we shall force all foreigners to leave our land."

121

"And the Rosks," Tyne added.

"*All* foreigners. Do you know there is a funeral to be held this evening, at the Bukit Besar? Do you know whose funeral it is? The half-Dutch girl, Mina."

"Mina! She's dead?" exclaimed Tyne.

"That is generally the reason for funerals," said Amir caustically. "The Rosks killed her because she had to do with your friend Mumford. Perhaps you will be interested to hear that the Rosks came for me yesterday; they tortured me. Perhaps today they will come back to kill me. You came to the Merdeka yesterday and I avoided you. Today I have not avoided you, and I shall probably die."

"Nonsense, Amir, take a grip of yourself! The Rosks won't want you again," Tyne said. "What did they ask you yesterday?"

Amir stopped crying as suddenly as he had begun. Looking Tyne straight in the eye, he pulled his bandaged arm from its sling and began to unwrap it. In a minute he produced it, exposing it with a penetrating mixture of horror and pride.

"The Rosks asked me where Murray Mumford is hiding," Amir said. "Because I did not tell them, this is what they did to me."

His left hand had been amputated at the wrist. Grafted on in its place, hanging limply, uselessly, was a chimpanzee's paw.

Tyne's own artificial left hand clenched convulsively in sympathetic pain.

"I'm sorry," he said. "I'm sorry, Amir."

"This is how they think of man."

He turned away, clumsily rebandaging his limb, and added in a choked voice, "But I did not tell them where Murray is. You I can tell. When he came here early yesterday morning, he said he was going to hide in the old Deli Jalat temple, down the lane. Now please go. Go and do not ever ask me anything again."

"I'm truly sorry," Tyne said, pausing by the door. "This'll be made up to you one day. Amir. Wait and see."

Amir did not turn round.

Outside, Tyne leapt straight over a low stone wall and crouched there with his gun out. Amir had given him a bigger shaking than he cared to admit to himself. Slowly he raised his head and looked about.

One or two natives were busy about the few dwellings facing onto the little back street into which he had emerged; none of them seemed to be interested in Murray. With a pang, he realized a bitter truth in what Amir had said. To the local population, the visiting nations which had descended upon Sumatra were as troublesome as the Rosks. Both groups were equally opposed to their way of life. The Rosks owed their ability to travel easily beyond their perimeter to a typically Eastern indifference to which of two forms of exploitation fell upon them. Had the

122

powerful Western nations behaved with more consideration to Sumatra over the past few centuries, they might be receiving more consideration from her now.

As Tyne was about to climb back over the wall, a man appeared from the direction of the Merdeka. He walked slowly as befitted his bulk, his eyes guardedly casting to left and right. It was Stobart.

He was walking away from the direction in which the Deli Jalat temple stood. When he saw the road was empty, he quickened his pace. As Tyne sank back into concealment, Stobart produced a whistle, raised it to his lips, blew it. No audible sound emerged; it was ultrasonic—no doubt a summoning of forces.

Directly the U.N.C. agent had gone, Tyne hopped back over the low wall and headed in the direction of the temple, where Murray had told Amir he was going to hide. The settlement with Murray was coming; in Tyne's pocket, the loaded gun felt reassuringly heavy.

Despite the hot sun on his shoulders, icy clarity seized him. He knew exactly what he was going to do. He was going to kill Murray.

Only one thing worried him, and he wasn't going to let that spoil his aim. Murray, waiting with his microfilm to meet the RPF agent, had covered his tracks well; the glimpse of Stobart (who had no doubt picked up Tyne's trail in the Merdeka lounge) was a token he was still at large, despite the none too scrupulous powers ranged against him. Yet Tyne, working alone, was on the point of finding him. Why?

Two pieces of information had led to Murray: Mina's information about the "plankton plant"; and from there, Amir's about the temple. Both U.N.C. and, presumably, Rosk had got the same lead from Mina; neither had got anything from Amir. Mina's information was capable of correct interpretation *only by Tyne*; Amir had said his piece voluntarily *only to Tyne*. Why?

One answer alone emerged. Murray had expected Tyne to pursue him. Before going into hiding, he had left those two messages with Mina and Amir deliberately *knowing Tyne would follow them up*. Yet Murray would realize Tyne could have only one reason for following: to avenge Allan Cunliffe's death on the moon. And the motives a man might have for silently, deviously, beckoning his murderer towards him remained notably obscure. And seductively obscure.

Murray must be made to explain before the stolen gun and the bought bullets had their way with him. He must explain—and of course he must yield up the vital microfilm; then he could die. Tyne experienced that touch of ice-cold clarity again. Once more he was right in the torrid zone of events. The equator of action whirled faster and faster about him; yet he could not feel a thing.

"Come in, sir. I will make enquiry about your friend from the priests," the wizened dwarf at the teak gate said. He pattered away on bare feet, crabbed and eager. Fallen women and white tuans especially welcome.

The Deli Jalat temple stood decaying in several acres of ground which were littered with past attempts to start chicken farms and scrap heaps. The central building was a not ignoble imitation of a late Hindu temple, highly ornamented, but round it had collected, like smashed cars round a road obstruction, a number of later erections, most of them flimsy affairs of lath or corrugated iron. These had never been immaculate; now they were merely tumble-down.

Unwilling to wait where he was bidden, Tyne moved over grass-encircled stones after the gatekeeper. In the air lingered an enchantingly sweet-sharp smell, a scent that seemed to carry with it its own unidentifiable emotion. There was a spice garden—grown out of hand, no doubt! close at hand. Turning a corner, Tyne came on a ramshackle covered way. At the far end, a woman in a Chinese dress, with clacking wooden soles on her feet, turned to look at him, then ran through a doorway. It looked like—yes, it had looked like Benda Ittai. Instinctively, Tyne increased his pace, sunlight jogging up and down on his shoulders.

He had a sudden choking image of taking her into the deserted spice garden, of making love to her there. It was not a picture he had intended. He turned his thoughts to Murray.

At the last door, the gatekeeper almost fell upon him with excitement, waving his arms anxiously.

"No sir, not here, sir! Stop by the gate, sir. Previously I ask you to wait. The priests will not be prepared—"

"I've not come to see the priests," Tyne said. Pushing the man aside, he stepped in, into the shade inside the building. It was as if the sunlight had rattled up like a blind, showing the room behind it: a cool room, all wood, except for two big stone vases in the middle of the floor. Three men, priests, with that vindictive, forward-leaning air that religion implants in the elderly, came forward at once.

"Please take me to Murray Mumford. I cannot wait." Tyne said.

"This is not a suitable hour," one of them said, ineffectually waving his hands.

"I'm sorry I cannot wait."

The three priests broke into a dialect, chattering rapidly to each other. They were frightened and angry. Fright won.

"Better follow me," one of them said, beckoning querulously at Tyne.

He led the way up broad and creaking stairs, on which a smell of cats floated. They passed down corridors of wood and corridors of stone, finally stopping by an insignificant door below another staircase. The priest unbarred this door and opened it. A short anteroom was revealed beyond, with two doors leading from it.

"Try the right door," suggested the priest.

As Tyne stepped inside, the priest slammed the door behind him. Left suddenly in semi-darkness, he moved, carefully over to the right-hand door; steadying himself, levelling the gun, he flung the door open.

It was a long, narrow room with a dirty window at one end. Occupying most of the space near the door was a wooden bed, now in use as a table and seat combined.

Benda Ittai, in a Chinese dress, stood alone in the middle of the room, her mouth slightly open in a *moue* of surprise.

"Come in, Mr. Todpuddle," she said, using the name Tyne had assumed when interrogated on Budo Budda's ketch.

He nodded to her, as if in brief acknowledgement of her beauty.

His hackles up, Tyne took one step inside the room. Murray Mumford stood behind the door, his hands raised above his head. Round his waist he wore a Space Service belt; a revolver protruded from its unbuttoned holster.

Tyne swung slowly on his heel, bringing his own revolver up to cover Murray's chest. He was aware of his face, stiff as leather, contorted into a killer's grin.

"Glad you finally made it, Tyne," Murray said, with a fair attempt at his old ease of manner. "Put your gun away and make yourself at home. Welcome to my humble—"

"Move over by the girl," Tyne said in a rasping whisper. "And I'll have your gun. Keep your hands raised. You're scum, Mumford—a betrayer, a traitor."

"If you hadn't got that toy in your hand, I'd break your neck for saying that," Murray said evenly, his cheeks colouring darkly.

"No, you wouldn't! Are you suggesting you aren't carrying information for the Rosks—information absolutely vital to Earth?"

Murray, keeping his hands raised, looked at Tyne straightly as he shuffled over towards Benda. His roughly handsome face looked tired and shadowy.

"If you want to discuss it, throw both the guns up on that high shelf," he said.

The shelf he referred to ran along one wall by the ceiling. Tyne never even glanced at it. He had the two of them together now, standing awkwardly by the foot of the bed.

"I don't want to discuss anything with you, Murray," he said.

"Go ahead and shoot me, then. But you probably realize as well as I do that one fool move like that and everything is lost."

"Give me that spool of microfilm, Murray."

"I've not got it!"

Tyne jerked his revolver convulsively. That he had not expected.

125

"Stop!" Benda Ittai made a nervous move forward. Though haggard, she still looked impressively cool and beautiful. "There is no time for quarrels, or we may be trapped here. Mr. Leslie, put both of the guns on the shelf and then we can explain to you. It is really necessary."

Tyne hesitated. He was in an awkward spot and he knew it. The vital matter was not his personal urge for revenge, but the need to get the film. The Rosk woman at least made it possible for him to back down, without losing too much face. Roughly, he snatched Murray's revolver from its holster and threw it up on the shelf with his own.

"Better," Murray said, lowering his hands and fumbling for mescahales. Tyne noted with satisfaction how those hands trembled as they lit the tube. His own hands—even his steel one—were trembling in the same way.

Taking the initiative again, he said to Benda, "I assume from your presence here that you are the Rosk agent Murray was told to meet?"

She said: "That is correct; as you know, I was held up." She smiled slightly, with satisfaction at the understatement.

Murray said: "You guess right; now stop guessing and listen to me. We may have very little time and we need your help."

"My help!" Tyne exploded. "I came here to kill you, Murray, by God, and now you tell me—"

Benda Ittai laid her hand on Tyne's arm. It felt soft and hot. 105.1, of course.

"Please give him a chance to explain!" she begged. "Don't talk so much: listen! Just listen!"

"Yes, sound advice to an ex-politician!" Murray said. He was quickly getting control of himself. Tyne also, savagely, wildly, took control of himself, sat on the edge of the plank bed and took a mescahale from Murray.

"Make it good," he said. "Make it very good."

"The microfilm must be handed to Miss Ittai," Murray said, "and she must get it to Sumatra Base, to the RPF there. Remember Tawdell Co Barr, the first Rosk to speak to Earth? He's the Peace Faction leader, secretly opposing Ap II Dowl. The RPF is weak; here is the one last chance to strengthen them to the point where they might overthrow Dowl. If they could show this microfilm, this proof of Dowl's bloody-mindedness, to a majority of the Rosks, the population would rise and rebel against the dictator."

"Our people are as human as yours," Benda broke in. "Please see this terrible business as a moral struggle rather than a detective game. When their eyes are opened to what is going on behind their backs, all my people will surely rise against Dowl."

"You're trying to tell me they don't know they're merely the advance party of an invasion?"

"Of course they don't. Can't you see," she said desperately, "we were all born on the ship, thinking ourselves colonists. There must have been sealed orders passed down from one generation of the officer class to the next."

"I see," Tyne said. He did see; this is how political manoeuvres must be carried out anywhere in the galaxy. The leaders plotted, and the rest followed like sheep—unless they could be roused to see that only muttonhood awaited them.

"You already have proof that I am no friend of Ap II Dowl and his ruffians," Benda said, speaking quietly, probably conscious of the effect she had upon Tyne. "Therefore trust me. Let me take the microfilm to my people, the RPF. There it will be used to more effect than if World Government got it. Can you see that?"

Yes, it was all clear enough, Tyne thought bitterly, knowing the other two were searching his face for a clue in advance to what he was going to say. He did not know what he was going to say. The issue—get the microfilm or bust!—had disintegrated as he approached it. Now he was faced with as ticklish a problem as ever he had met across the highly polished tables of the U.N.C.

If he did nothing—say, if he were shot—Under-Secretary Grierson would start the machinery grinding. The small Rosk force on Earth would be crushed before reinforcements arrived. And when they did arrive? Why, they would presumably be merciless; nuclear bombardment from space did not bear thinking of.

If Stobart and his men arrived here, they of course would take the microfilm without delay; they would find it wherever it was concealed. It would never go near a Rosk again. That move would also entail an immediate counter-attack against the perfidious alien within the gates.

If Ap II Dowl's men arrived here first—well, that was obviously the worst alternative of all.

At present, however, the initiative was not with Grierson, Stobart or Dowl; it was with Tyne. Fleetingly, he remembered the Theory of Irresponsible Activity he had formulated; he must have been light-headed at the time. Here he was faced with the weightiest problem of all time; how was he to resolve it for what would ultimately prove the best?

Turning towards the window, he gazed irritably out through the dusty panes, to hide his indecision from Murray and the girl. In the bright landscape outside, something moved. A man—or a Rosk—had dodged from one clump of bushes to another. Tyne's time was running low.

Abruptly, he turned back into the dull room. The RPF ought to have knowledge of the invasion plans, as Benda suggested; the more dissension sown in Sumatra Base, the better. Equally, Earth must have the details; then, they could be prepared for eventualities.

"A copy must be made of the microfilm, Miss Ittai," he said. "The U.N.C. will keep the copy to study. You will then be given safe conduct to slip back into your base with the original, to hand over to Tawdell Co Barr."

He turned to Murray, sitting now on the edge of the bed, stubbing out his mescahale.

"As you observed, time is short," he said. "Give me the microfilm quickly."

"You don't seem to take a point too well," Murray said. He rubbed his eyes, looking tired and irritable: it was as if he had suddenly realized that whether he personally triumphed now or not, life would ultimately triumph over him—impersonally, of course, but with as little remorse as if the issue were a personal one! "Lord Almighty, Tyne, isn't it obvious to you what a fool you are being? As I told you, I haven't got the microfilm."

The bent figures running behind bushes—they would be straightening up now, perhaps making a last dash for the temple. And there was Allan Cunliffe, permanently straightened up, stiff as a stick. The two images, spears of urgency and anger, struck at Tyne's mind. He flung himself at Murray.

Murray got half up, then fell back under the assault. They crashed together onto the bed. The middle of it fell through, pitching them onto the floor. Tyne rolled on top of Murray. Doubled up, Murray ground his knee into Tyne's solar plexus. Tyne brought his steel hand chopping down on the side of Murray's neck. Blue about the lips, Murray subsided.

"That'll settle . . . your . . ." Tyne gasped. He had been badly winded. Blobs of colour waved like flags before his eyes. He shook his head to get the knocking sound out of it, before realizing that someone was actually hammering on the door.

Looking up amid the ruins of the big bed, he saw Benda Ittai—but through a haze—open the door; one of the priests entered, speaking urgently to her. After a minute, she ran over to Tyne.

"The enemy are surrounding this building!" she said. "The priests have seen them. Quickly, we must get away! I have a helicopter concealed outside. Come along!"

Seizing his good hand in her hot one, she pulled him to his feet. Murray groaned to himself as the weight shifted off him. Dazedly, Tyne allowed himself to be dragged from the room as the priest led them out. They trotted through the labyrinth of the building, Tyne gradually regaining his wits as they went. As they left the temple, he recalled that he had left his gun behind. It was too late to go back.

They emerged into a secluded courtyard surrounded by small cells once inhabited by novices. The whole place was slowly crumbling; it might have been built of old bread. Heat as choking as regret lay in the well of the mossy buildings. Under a stretched canopy of some camouflage material stood a small, trim helicopter. Benda ran across to it. She pressed one corner of the canopy and the whole thing collapsed, snapped up together like a blind. Picking it up, business-like, the girl stowed it into the helicopter and swung herself up.

She had an attractive pair of legs, Tyne thought. His powers of observation and deduction were returning. Even the sick feeling in his stomach was fading.

He pulled himself into the seat beside her as the priest backed bowing into the temple. At once, Benda started the rotors moving. They could see the disturbed heat move in whirlpools round them. Big green lizards scuttled for safety in the courtyard.

"Look!" Tyne shouted, pointing.

Over the top of a row of cells, a head appeared. Then shoulders. Then a rifle, swinging down to point into the helicopter. Rosk or man? Did Benda know? All she had said in the temple was, "The enemy are surrounding us." By that, she might have meant Ap II Dowl's toughs, or Stobart's. Which indicated the ambiguity of the role she played.

Almost jabbing her elbow into Tyne's ribs. Benda thrust her hand down into a capacious pocket. She had one of those murderous .88's there. Whipping it round, leaning half out of the cabin, she took a pot-shot at the sniper on the roof.

She missed.

Tyne saw the ridge of the roof shatter, spraying bits of tile into the sniper's face. His rifle went off wildly as he flung his hands up to his bleeding mouth. Then the helicopter began to rise.

As they began to bucket upwards, a man ran from the temple into the bright sunlight. It was Stobart, his face blistered with sweat, his great body heaving with exertion. Although he clasped a gun in one hand, he made no attempt to shoot; instead he was bellowing at Tyne, beckoning him savagely. Not a word came through the blanketing roar of the rotors above them.

"Just away in time!" Benda called.

Rising speedily above the ramshackled knot of temple buildings, they slanted eastward and saw ant-sized men run into the open. Their shadow fled across the ants. The ants were firing upwards, fruitlessly.

VII

Mopping his face, Tyne thought hard. It was obvious enough that the charming Miss Ittai, far from having saved his life again, as he had at first believed to be the case, had tricked him into getting into the helicopter. She had wanted, for reasons of her own, to get him away from his own people. His brain was still muzzy from the effect of Murray's knee in his stomach; savagely, he shook his head. Fuzzy he might be, but on several points he was clear enough. And one of them was: this little beauty was heading in the direction of the Roskian Sumatra Base as fast as she could go.

A little, round cloud formed ahead, and another beyond that. They hit turbulence and lumped heavily up and down. Someone below had an anti-flight gun trained on them.

Tyne looked down, but could see only roads and plantations. All round the outskirts of Padang, the U.N.C. Force had pockets of fortification and defence. Stobart must have worked quickly in getting onto them. In a minute, Tyne thought, interceptors would be up after them. He did not relish the idea.

The same thought had occurred to the girl. Grimly, she was knocking every last spark of power out of the machine. Another crumpling explosion outside sent them rocking sideways. Locking the controls on a climbing course, she turned to Tyne. Suddenly, the gun was in her hand again.

"I hate to do this, but you must realize I will do anything to succeed, anything," she said. "This mission must be carried through at all costs. Beside it, none of us matter at all. If you so much as move suspiciously I will kill you. I will have to kill you."

"You know, you interest me, Benda," Tyne said. "Why couldn't you have fallen in with the scheme for duplicating the microfilm I suggested back in the temple?"

She smiled dismissively. "Do you really think your people would let you, me or the film go, once they had us? You are really an amateur, Tyne."

"I've heard that said before, thanks. What do you want me to do?"

The craft bucked furiously, as he asked. Hanging on, keeping the gun fixed on him, Benda said, "It is getting rough. We are probably being pursued so you must bail out. There is one of our mini-rotor kits behind you, which is the equivalent of your parachutes. Put it on, jump! That will be a distraction to the U.N.C. Forces. Possibly when they see you are going down, they will cease to chase me. Also, this little flier will travel faster without you."

"You have it all worked out," Tyne said admiringly. "And it can't be far to the Rosk base now. Anything else you want before I go?"

Her gun waved a little.

"Yes," she said. "Unscrew your false hand and give it to me."

A wave of something like triumph ran over Tyne. So at last he had guessed, and guessed rightly. Benda had "rescued" him for the same reason that Murray had deliberately left him a trail to follow: because Tyne was absolutely essential to their plan. All the time he had seemed to be on the fringe of events, he had been at the centre.

Murray had wanted a safe hiding place for the microfilm, somewhere where his contact could still get them even if he were intercepted. So when Tyne was unconscious on the trip back from Luna Area 101, it had been an easy matter for him to slip the little spool inside the cavity of one of Tyne's steel fingers. Then he had played on Tyne's feelings harshly enough to ensure the latter followed him, made himself conveniently accessible! All the time that Tyne had presumed himself to be acting under free will, to be daring all in the name of action, his moves had been calculated long in advance by someone else. The puppet had danced, unconscious of its strings.

Reading the anger and resentment on Tyne's face, Benda jerked the gun at him in warning.

"Fire!" he said. "For God's sake, fire, girl! I'm less of an amateur than you think. When I thought about it, it was obvious why you left Murray behind at the temple instead of me; before I broke in on the pair of you, he told you what he'd done about hiding the film, didn't he?"

"I'm sorry," she said. "You were rather sweet." Shutting her eyes, she fired at point blank range. He watched her little fist contract as she squeezed the trigger.

Tyne opened his good hand, showing her a palm full of the semi-self-propelled bullets.

"I emptied your gun while you were playing with the controls. I thought you might be dangerous; I was right, wasn't I?"

Unexpectedly, she burst into tears; they looked much like any girl's tears. Tyne did not realize at the time the relief those tears expressed; relief both at having done her duty and at having been baulked of the necessity for taking life. Pulling the gun from her hand, Tyne reloaded and thrust it into his own pocket.

Now he turned his attention to the helicopter.

The anti-flight barrage had dropped behind. They were over jungle now, still gaining height. Screwing his eyes against the sun's glare, Tyne peered back into the blue sky. Scudding behind them, a V-shape moved low over the variegated cover, gaining, climbing. It was a manned interceptor, coming after them fast.

It seemed to be a case of get down or be shot down. Tyne grabbed the controls, angling the rotors, letting them slide down the sky. He felt only exhilaration at that moment.

Away ahead, blue, hazy, an egg stuck out of the broken wash of landscape. It was the grounded Alpha II ship. They were that near Rosk Base! Tyne growled with a sort of pleasure. At least he had saved himself a visit there. Moreover, although at the eleventh hour, he had saved the situation; Benda sat helpless beside him, suddenly drained of will. He was in control now.

He felt more than heard the interceptor come up. Tyne jogged the wheel, letting them sideslip—but not out of danger. An aircharge burst above the cabin. The controls went dead instantly, their vital elements fused.

Tyne cursed as the helicopter jerked over onto its back, clouting his head against a brace. For a moment he became detached from the scene, watching as from a long distance while the Rosk girl wrenched helplessly at the panel. Then the jungle spun up, and he snapped back into full possession of his sense. They were about to crash!

"Hang on!" he yelled.

So he was in control, was he?—And this was what being in control consisted of: hanging on!

They struck!

In the terrifying concussion, shreds of pulpy green stuff flew everywhere. The helicopter split like matchwood. Yet they were lucky. They had crashed into a thicket of giant cactus, some pillars of which reared twenty-five feet high. The stuff acted like a great pulpy cushion, breaking their fall.

Groaning, Tyne rolled over. Benda sprawled on top of him. Dragging her with him, still groaning with mingled shock and relief, Tyne crawled out of the debris, pushed his way painfully through shattered cacti, and stood up. Groggily, he looked round him.

The helicopter had crashed on an old lava bed. Rutted and furrowed, it supported little in the way of vegetation except for the occasional thicket of cactus, which crept tenaciously along fault lines. It was as forbidding a landscape as could be imagined. A quarter of a mile away stood a low rampart: the fortified perimeter of Sumatra Base. Directly he saw it, Tyne dropped to his knees. It did not do to come within range of that place.

As he was trying to drag the unconscious girl behind a cactus cliff, a shadow swooped across him. The interceptor was coming in to land. It amazed him that there was till no activity from the Rosk base; they had been known to fire on any Earth plane flying so near the perimeter. Settling Benda down as comfortably as he could, Tyne ran back to meet his pursuer.

The interceptor had landed tail first on its buffers. Already the pilot was picking his way over the uneven ground towards Tyne; although his head was bent as he watched his footing over the lava, Tyne recognized him. Dodging behind some nearby columns of cactus, he drew Benda's gun and waited in ambush for him.

"Raise your hands!" he said, as the man appeared.

Startled, Allan Cunliffe did as he was told.

"You don't have to aim that thing at me, Tyne," he said quietly. He bit his lips and looked round anxiously.

"I think I do," Tyne replied. "Until about ten minutes ago, I thought you were dead; now I want a few explanations from you."

"Didn't Murray tell you I was still alive?"

"No, Murray didn't have time to tell me much. I worked this one out for myself, believe it or not. As soon as I knew Murray had tricked me into following him around, I guessed his tale about shooting you on Luna was a lie, the carrot that kept me going like a donkey; I had thought it unlikely to begin with. Obviously that means you're as implicated as he. Take your belt off."

"My trousers will fall down."

"Keep clear of the cactus then!"

"You're not pleased to see me, Tyne; you're all mixed up."

"So mixed up I trust no one. I regard you as an enemy, Allan."

Tyne took the belt and began to tie Allan's hands behind his back. As he worked, Allan talked, protesting.

"Listen, Tyne, you can trust me, just as you always could. Do you think I'd work for the Rosks in any way? I'll tell you this: I was a U.N.C. agent before I ever met you—even before I joined the Space Service. And I can prove I'm an agent. Look, the two men who caught up with you at the plankton plant, and were in the car when the fly-spy appeared—"

"Dickens and the dumb fellow?" Tyne asked. "What about them?"

"*I* was the dumb one, Tyne! I had to keep masked and silent or you'd have recognized me."

Allan stood there helpless now, his trousers sagging down to his knees. In sudden fury, Tyne pushed him over and knelt by him, grabbing his shirt in his fist.

"You bastard, Allan! *Why* couldn't you have spoken? Why've I had to go round in the dark all the time, nobody helping me?"

Allan tried to roll away from him, his face black.

"You still had to think I was dead then, in case you gave up the hunt for Murray," he said. "Time was short; we wanted you to keep driving ahead. Don't you see that when Dickens had given you a spot of necessary information, we were going to *let* you escape!"

"You could be lying now!"

"Why should I lie? You must have that microfilm now—you reached Murray; all that's needed is to get it to U.N.C. as quickly as possible. Hand it over to me and let's get back to safety."

Tyne's heart jumped. So Allan—once his friend, now (caught in the no-man's land of intrigue) his rival—did not know how Murray had concealed the invasion plans. Grabbing him by his jacket front, Tyne dragged him until they were behind a cactus clump, out of sight of the Rosk base, still surprisingly silent and menacing.

"Tell me what happened on Area 101 when I was laid low," he demanded. "When you were supposed to have been killed."

"It's no secret," Allan said. "You went out like a light when you were hit on the shoulder. Murray and I tried to carry you back to the ship and of course the Rosks caught us and disarmed us. There were only three of them—did you know that?—but in their far more efficient suits, they made rings round us. They told us that they and the fellow manning the searchlight were the only members of the peace faction, the RPF, supporting Tawdell Co Barr on Luna. But they'd managed to filch these plans; that was easy enough. The trouble was to get them to Earth—they were all three already under suspicion.

"When we heard the facts from them, Murray volunteered to take the spool to their Padang contact. To make sure he did so, they said they would hold me hostage. I watched Murray drag you back into the ship and leave."

"How did you get away from them?" Tyne asked suspiciously.

"I didn't. They let me go of their own accord after a while. At first I thought it was for the reason they gave, that they could not keep me concealed anywhere from Ap II Dowl's secret police; but it wasn't. They wanted me loose so that I could set the World Government forces onto Murray. I made full pelt for U.N.C. HQ Luna in the stolen lunarider they gave me, and got through to Double K Four—the agent you know by the name of Stobart. By the time he picked you up in the bar of the Roxy, he had heard from me and knew roughly what was going on. Then I got back to Padang myself as quickly as possible, meeting up with Stobart and Dickens. By then—"

"Wait a minute," Tyne said.

He could hear a whine growing louder in the sky. He had been listening for it. Other interceptors were heading this way. Allan looked up with hope in his eyes. Tyne had less than five minutes left.

"I don't know what you're talking about," he said roughly to Allan. "You tell me these Roskian pacifists let you go so that you could set our people onto Murray, just when everything depended on his getting through? How do you make sense of that?"

"The whole business was staged to look as if everything depended on Murray's getting through. In fact, those RPF boys were clever; they wanted Murray caught with the film on him. They never intended anything but that the plans should fall into Earth hands. If Murray had double-crossed them, so much the better. Of course, Tawdell's agent here, the girl Ittai, didn't know that; she went to meet Murray in all good faith."

"Why go such a long way round about? Why didn't they just post the film, once they had stolen it, direct to U.N.C.?"

Allan laughed briefly.

134

"And who'd have believed it? You know how the political situation stands. If the film had been sent direct to us, it would probably have been dismissed as just another of Ap II Dowl's threats. The Area 101 RPF had even planted that strange object we had to investigate outside their dome as a bait; we happened to be the mice who came and sniffed at the cheese."

Tyne stood up. He could see the interceptors now, three of them flying low. At any minute now, they would see the crashed helicopter and be coming down.

"You've made yourself clear," he said to Allan. "The whole episode has been a twist from start to finish, and I've had to take most of the twisting. Only one thing isn't clear to me."

Hopefully, Allan propped himself on one elbow and asked what that was.

"I don't know who I can trust but myself. Everyone else is playing a subtle double game."

"You can trust Stobart, even if you refuse to trust me. He should be in one of those three interceptors."

"I trust nobody, not even that fat slob Stobart!"

Stooping, he wrenched Allan's trousers off, tied them savagely round his ankles.

"Sweat it out, feller!" he advised. "Yours pals will be down in a couple of minutes to put your pants on. And don't forget to look after Benda Ittai. She's over by the crash. Meanwhile, I'm borrowing your machine."

Ignoring Allan's shouts, he ran across the lava bed to the grounded interceptor. The other planes were wheeling overhead. As he pulled himself into the swing seat, the radio was calling.

". . . Why don't you answer? What's happening down there?" It was Stobart's voice, harsh but recognizable.

Puffing, assuming Allan's voice as well as he could, Tyne flipped the speech switch and said, "Regret delay . . . fight with Leslie . . I've got him tied up . . . Come on down."

"Have you got the microfilm? Murray Mumford reports that it's in Tyne's false hand."

"I haven't got it. Come on down," Tyne said, cutting the voice off. Switching on the feed, he tensed himself and eased in the jets. Rocking skywards, the interceptor responded perfectly; Tyne had flown these machines back in his training days.

With joy, he thought of the indecision that must be clouding Stobart's mind. Yes, Stobart would be suspicious. But Stobart would have to land to discover what was going on. Tyne found himself hoping that the guns of the Rosk base would open up. Just to give the agent a scare.

He checked the fuel, finding his tanks almost full. Excellent; he could get to Singapore, centre of World Government, in one hop.

135

He was not going to unscrew his steel fist for anyone less than Governor-General Hjanderson of the U.N.C.

VIII

It was, and the most scrupulous person must agree, a beautiful cell; commodious, with toilet and bathroom (complete with shower and massage unit) attached, it was furnished in impeccable if uninspired taste, and provided with books, visicube and pictures; there was air-conditioning, there was concealed lighting, but it was still a cell.

The food was excellent and Tyne had eaten well. The couch comfortable and Tyne had slept well. The carpet was deep, and Tyne now walked restlessly back and forth upon it.

His left hand was missing.

He had been confined here for twenty hours. Arriving in Singapore shortly after two o'clock on the previous afternoon, he had been arrested at once, interrogated at length and shut in here. His questioners had been civil, removing his steel hand sympathetically even apologetically. Since then, all his wants had been ministered to, and his patience had been exhausted.

A knock came at the door. They knocked! It seemed the ultimate in irony. A slender man with a face the colour of an old pocket, dressed in a faultless suit, entered and attempted to smile at Tyne.

"Would you be so kind as to step this way to see Governor Purdoe?" he asked.

Tyne saved his wrath, carrying it almost gleefully behind the minion until he was ushered into a large, bare room where a uniformed octogenarian rose from behind a desk. This was Prison Governor Purdoe, a watchful man with a watchful smile arranged on his apple-clean face.

"How much longer am I going to be locked up here?" Tyne demanded, marching up to his desk. "When am I going to see Hjanderson? What the devil do you want to talk to me about?"

"I am the governor of this institute," the old man said reprovingly, without removing his smile.

"Let's not bring class into this. All I want to know is am I or am I not a bloody hero? If I am, is this the sort of treatment you think I enjoy?"

"You are indeed a hero, Mr. Leslie," the governor said placatingly, "Nobody denies it. Please sit down and smoke a mescahale and let some of the blood drain out of your head."

Governor Purdoe came round from behind the desk. He stood in front of Tyne, looking at him until he seated himself; then he said, "It may console you to know that your two associates in this affair, Murray Mumford and Allan Cunliffe, are also detained here. We are not sitting idly by. Your stories are being correlated."

"All I'm saying is that there was no need to place me under lock and key to start with. I came here voluntarily, didn't I?"

The governor inclined his grey head.

"When you arrived, there was a general U.N.C. call out for you, dead or alive. You were fortunate, Mr. Leslie, that we managed to get you and keep you safely before less enlightened parties reached you. An agent whom I believe you know as Stobart had reason to fear, when you tricked him yesterday, that you might have turned traitor. He merely took the precautions expected of him."

"Don't mention Stobart to me, Governor! It brings me out in a rash. Just tell me what you wanted me for. Can I have a fist back?"

Governor Purdoe smiled a little bleakly. Seen close to, the smile was not attractive.

"Shortly," he said. "I summoned you here because I wanted in general to tell you that you are in the best place here—that far from being neglected, you are the prime mover in a lot of intense activity, most of which necessarily remains secret, even from you —and in particular to tell you that Governor-General Hjanderson will come to thank you personally as soon as possible. We believe you acted with excellent intentions, you see."

Snorting, Tyne stubbed out his mescahale on the shiny desk top and jumped up. He topped Purdoe by a head, but the latter never moved.

"Governments!" he snapped. "You people are all alike! Diplomacy and suspicion—nothing but! Nobody trusting anybody! Don't you take anything that happens at its face value?"

"You have run into a lot of trouble because you did just that," the governor said. He turned away, walked round behind his desk, sat down with a hint of tiredness. His manicured right hand performed a gesture of contempt. "There is no trust anywhere, Leslie. I regret it as much as you, but I face the fact. None of you young men are realists. These plans for the invasion from Alpha Centauri II—not a word about them must escape; that is just one good reason for your continuing to stay with us. Try—please try to think less of yourself, and reflect instead on the grave issues looming behind these plans. Sithers, conduct our guest back to his—room."

The man with the dirty linen face came forward. Tyne shrugged his shoulders, making hopelessly towards the door; he knew he would get nothing out of Purdoe even if he squeezed him like a sponge. He had met the institutional type before.

In the doorway he paused.

"Just tell me one tiny, weeny little state secret, governor," he begged. "All that tale Allan Cunliffe told me about the Rosks really manoeuvring to get the microfilm in our hands—was that true or false?"

An odd expression—it might have been another smile—passed over the governor's face and vanished.

"Cunliffe has been an excellent agent for a number of years," he said, "and, though I grant you it does not necessarily follow, everything he told you was perfectly correct. The RPF wanted us to get the invasion plans. However, there was one minor point he missed, because he could not possibly have known it. The invasion plans themselves are probably false."

The rest of that day passed with intolerable slowness for Tyne.

He reflected, as the governor had urged him to do, on the grave issues behind the Rosk invasion plans. One issue at least stuck out a mile. There had been no proof as yet that Alpha II's technology was far in advance of Earth's in this last decade of the twenty-second century: even the construction of a gigantic interstellar ship was, in theory, at least, not beyond Earth's resources. But an interstellar invasion implied many things. It implied, surely, some form of faster-than-light communication between Ap II Dowl's force and Alpha II. It implied, too, a drive a good deal faster than the one professedly used to get the first ship here, for no invasion would be feasible between planets a two-generations' journey apart. It implied, undoubtedly, an integration of planetary resources vastly superior to anything Earth dreamed of, split as it was into numerous fractious nations. It implied, above all, an overwhelming confidence in success; as vast an undertaking as an interstellar invasion would never get under way unless the powers behind it considered it a fool-proof scheme.

The picture was not, Tyne admitted to himself, anything but gloomy. The role he had played in it shrank into the mere prologue to a whole volume of catastrophe.

But if the plans were false?

What did that mean? Had the RPF been tricked, perhaps, into believing that the belligerent forces would do one thing, whereas actually they intended to do another? Tyne sitting hour after hour in his so comfortable, so commodious cell, could invent many such unhelpful questions to ask himself. Only the answers were beyond him.

If he disliked not knowing the answers, he disliked knowing the questions even more.

On the third day of Tyne's imprisonment he was summoned again to the governor's presence. He appeared in chastened mood before the old man.

"I've had no news," he said. "What's the general situation? Are the Rosks making a move?"

"The situation has changed very radically since we last met," Purdoe said, his face crumpling into innumerable pleats as he smiled. "And may I say, Mr. Leslie, how glad I am that you no longer come into here clamouring for release. You have been thinking, I take it?"

Tyne sighed.

"I'm not really a man of action, governor, but that doesn't mean you have to be avuncular with me. What have you brought me here for this time?"

"Take a mescahale, young man. The Governor-General of the U.N.C., Mr. Hjanderson, is here to see you; and I should advise you to watch your tongue for the occasion. Now please excuse me for a minute."

He disappeared through a rear door with his sprightly old man's gait. To kill time, Tyne stared at the linen-faced attendant who had brought him here; the attendant fingered his tie and coughed.

Hjanderson, when he appeared, was instantly recognizable: dapper, fifty-ish, a little like a wolf with an expense account, smelling agreeably of the most fashionable shaving soap. He shook hands briskly with Tyne and sat down facing him, palms pressed on knees.

"I promised to come and see you," he said, "and I have kept that promise. I regret it has taken me so long to do so. These have been days of crisis. Very grave crisis."

"I'm pleased if I have been of any service. Perhaps I can have my hand back now, sir."

Hjanderson brushed most of this aside.

"Service? Yes, Leslie, I think you played your part as you saw it. You were never more than partially in the picture, you know. We have received a great deal of help from the Roskian girl, Benda Ittai, who you left for dead beside her crashed helicopter."

With an effort, Tyne swallowed this blatant misrepresentation; his term with the U.N.C. had accustomed him to such gambits.

"Apart from the fact that I did not leave her for dead, how is she? Where is she?" he asked.

"She is radiant; she is here," Purdoe said, interrupting, coming up from behind his desk. With his thin, veined hand he touched—for whatever privately submerged reason of his own—the arm of the fur coat Benda wore, as he ushered her through the rear doorway and into the office.

"Benda!" Tyne exclaimed. Forgetting the Governor-General of the U.N.C., he went over to her and took her hands. Hot; 105.1; alien; but beautiful, and smiling in most tender fashion. He couldn't let her get away with it so easily.

"Haven't seen you since you tried to shoot me," he said affably.

"The situation has changed," she said, still smiling. The tormented look she had worn when putting him ashore on the island

139

had entirely gone now.

"Since you appear to have lost interest in the political situation," Hjanderson said dryly, rising to his feet, "it remains for me only to tell you that you are now a free man, Mr. Leslie. Moreover, I think I can mention that it is possible you may eventually get some sort of decoration; the E.D.C.E., probably."

"I'll wear it all the time," Tyne promised, "but before you go, please tell me about the invasion—what's happening, what's been done about it?"

"Miss Ittai can tell you the details," Hjanderson said smiling and extending a sharp hand. "Now you must excuse me; I have a news conference to attend. I am, of course delighted to have been able to see you. I wish you good luck for the future."

"Of course," Tyne murmured vaguely. He turned to Benda before Purdoe had shown the Governor-General out. "I'd prefer to ask you this over a restaurant table, but what's been happening that I don't know about?"

"Perhaps the table can be arranged later," she said. "From now on—whether that is what I want or not—I am on your side of the fence. I cannot go back to my people. That is why I have told the Governor-General the truth as I have found it to be.

"The invasion plans, as I think you have heard, are false. And not they only. The RPF also was a spurious organization! Don't mistake me—a lot of its members genuinely wished for peace between Rosk and Man as I did and still do myself. But Tawdell Co Barr is, and must always have been, a puppet of Ap II Dowl's. No doubt we should all have been wiped out when we had served our purpose."

"Budo Budda was out to kill you as it was," Tyne said.

"Oh quite; I was merely expendable, I fear. Even Budda would not have known the RPF was a dummy front—otherwise he would not have been after Murray. Only Ap II and Tawdell Co Barr are supposed to know."

"And how did you find out?"

She shrugged her shoulders, her face puckered as she recalled that horrible moment of revelation.

"For some time, small events in the Base had made me suspicious, but I really knew what was happening when we crashed near Sumatra Base and they neither opened fire on us nor sent a party out to pick us up. Their silence could mean only one thing: the plans were intended only for U.N.C. eyes. They were false, designed only to scare Earth."

"They certainly did that," Tyne agreed. "This clears up one point that has been bothering me. I'd been wondering what this spool of microfilm was doing on Luna in the first place. Obviously it was planted there where its journey to your base would attract maximum attention."

Benda Ittai began to look moist about the eyes, as the treachery of her fellow beings struck her afresh. Turning to Purdoe, who stood sympathetically by, Tyne asked, "What was Ap II Dowl's idea in all this?"

With a barely perceptible gesture, Purdoe led Tyne to the other side of the room.

"This is all very sad for the young woman," he said in an official voice. "You see the invasion scare was Dowl's last bluff. When confronted in the Council with our knowledge of the plans, he would probably have said that he would call the attacking fleet off if we'd give him all Sumatra, or perhaps Africa as well, or half the globe, or whatever his megalomaniac mind conceived. He's got nothing to back a real threat, Leslie. This was pure bluff from start to finish. You were really ill-advised, if I may say so, to get mixed up in it."

"We've all been chasing around risking our necks," Tyne said testily, "just to serve Dowl's purpose. But how are you so *sure* it's all bluff?"

For answer, the governor pulled a message form from his pocket and unfolded it daintily. Tyne recognized the flimsy as a signal which had come through secret governmental channels.

"This arrived just before I summoned you," Purdoe said. "Please read it. You will find it enlightening."

The message read: "Circulation: Govt Levels A-C only and List 566 as specified. Text begins: Hoyle Observatory, Luna, confirms Alpha Centauri about to go nova. Increase to apparent magnitude Minus One expected by end of year. This temperature rise will be sufficient to render life on its planets untenable. Authoritative circles confirm that first signs of nova effect would have been observable locally three generations ago in sunspot and radio phenomena. Rosk ship may therefore be regarded as lifeboat; no doubt other lifeboats despatched to other nearby systems. Therefore chances of invasion now highly improbable, repeat highly improbable. Suggested course of action: summit announcement of text of this action, with warning to Ap II Dowl to settle down or move on. Text ends. 10/10/2193 Luna-Singa-Beam Y."

Tyne put the flimsy down, slowly, blankly. Round his head ran some lines from an historical solid, the name of which eluded him: 'Thus enterprises of great pith and moment, With this regard their currents turn wary, And lose the name of action." Was it Shakespeare? He was confused; from the diplomatic point of view, this, of course, was a triumph. The Rosks stood revealed in all their weakness, and could now be squashed as Earth saw fit. Yet in Tyne's head, the picture of oceans steaming, babies cooking slowly in cellars, planets gradually turning to ashes, seemed to him something less than a happy ending.

"I must say I have marked you down," Governor Purdoe said,

regarding Tyne coldly, "as rather a hard and impertinent young man. How typical of your generation that you should have no reaction to this great news!"

"Good heavens!" Tyne exclaimed. "I was just thinking—"

"Forgive me if I interrupt; no doubt you were thinking of your own personal glory; I can read you like a book. When Governor-General Hjanderson gave you your freedom, I hoped it meant you would leave here at once. Will you please do so now? And one thing—please take Miss Ittai with you. I understand she has formed an attachment for you; for me, that will always remain the ultimate proof of Roskian misguidedness."

Tyne looked hard at the old man, so neat, so smiling. With unexpected self-control, he swallowed his anger. He wanted to say that it would be impossible to understand a Rosk as long as it was impossible to understand a man, but the words did not come. There were no words; he realized he could comprehend Purdoe no more than Purdoe comprehended him.

Frustratedly, he turned to Benda Ittai. Here at least was someone worth trying to comprehend.

He felt like spending a life at it.

"Let's go and find that restaurant table I was telling you about," he said, taking her arm.

She smiled at him. It was a very comprehensible smile.

NEL BESTSELLERS

F.2373	THE DOCTOR DARES	Elizabeth Seifert 5/-
F.2231	THE NEW DOCTOR	Elizabeth Seifert 4/-
F.2159	HARRIET HUME	Rebecca West 5/-

Science Fiction

F.1233	THE OCTOBER COUNTRY	Ray Bradbury 3/6
F.1234	THE SMALL ASSASSIN	Ray Bradbury 3/6
F.1803	STARSHIP TROOPERS	Robert Heinlein 5/-
F.2124	STRANGER IN A STRANGE LAND	Robert Heinlein 7/6

War

F.2423	STRIKE FROM THE SKY—THE BATTLE OF BRITAIN STORY
		Alexander McKee 6/-
F.1686	EASTERN APPROACHES	Fitzroy Maclean 7/6
F.1875	THE LONGEST DAY (illustrated)	Cornelius Ryan 7/6
F.2146	THE LAST BATTLE (illustrated)	Cornelius Ryan 12/6
F.1270	THE RED BERET	Hilary St. George Saunders 5/-
F.1943	REPORT FROM No. 24	Gunnar Sonsteby 5/-
F.1084	THE GUNS OF AUGUST—AUGUST 1914	Barbara W. Tuchman 5/-
F.1880	END QUIET WAR	Hedger Wallace 5/-

Western

F.2134	AMBUSH	Luke Short 3/6
F.2135	CORONER CREEK	Luke Short 3/6
F.2142	THE ALAMO	Lon Tinkle 3/6
F.2063	THE SHADOW SHOOTER	W. C. Tuttle 3/6
F.2132	THE TROUBLE TRAILER	W. C. Tuttle 3/6
F.2133	MISSION RIVER JUSTICE	W. C. Tuttle 3/6
F.2180	SILVER BUCKSHOT	W. C. Tuttle 3/6

General

F.2420	THE SECOND SEX	Simone De Beauvoir 8/6
F.2117	NATURE OF THE SECOND SEX	Simone De Beauvoir 5/-
F.2234	SEX MANNERS FOR MEN	Robert Chantham 5/-
F.2060	SEX AND THE ADOLESCENT	Maxine Davis 5/-
F.2136	WOMEN	John Philip Lundin 5/-
F.2333	MISTRESSES	John Philip Lundin 5/-
F.2382	SECRET AND FORBIDDEN	Paul Tabori 8/6
U.2366	AN ABZ OF LOVE	Inge and Sten Hegeler 10/6
F.2374	SEX WITHOUT GUILT	Albert Ellis Ph.D. 8/6
F.2358	CANDY	Southern and Hoffenberg 10/6
F.2511	SEXUALIS '95	Jacques Sternberg 5/-

Mad

S.2955	A MAD LOOK AT OLD MOVIES	3/6
S.3523	BOILING MAD	4/6
S.3496	THE MAD ADVENTURES OF CAPTAIN KLUTZ	4/6
S.3158	THE QUESTIONABLE MAD	3/6
S.2385	FIGHTING MAD	3/6
S.3268	HOWLING MAD	3/6
S.3413	INDIGESTIBLE MAD	3/6

NEL P.O. BOX 11, FALMOUTH, CORNWALL

Please send cheque or postal order. Allow 9d. per book to cover postage and packing (Overseas 1/- per book).

Nàme...

Address ....

....

Title ....
(MARCH)